Károly Akos
Magda Akos:

DINA

A Mother Practises Conductive Education (Petö System)

A plea for personal responsibility and action by parents of children with cerebral palsy

Edited by Gabriele Haug

This edition is a co-puplication of the Foundation for Conductive Educa-
tion,Birmingham, UK and Alabanda-Verlag Ulm, Germany
1991
Graphic design: Elisabeth Kaas , Ulm
Cover design: Julie Proctor, Birmingham
Photosetting: N.C.H. Verlag, Konstanz
Printing: Maus Offset-Druck, Konstanz

Károly Ákos
Magda Ákos

Dina

Edited by
Gabriele Haug

A Mother Practises
Conductive Education
(Petö System)

A plea for personal
responsibility and action
by parents of children
with cerebral palsy

Acknowledgements

The text was translated by Susanne Schuster

Editorial help was given by Dr Steve Iliffe, Department of Primary Health Care, Whittington Hospital, London N 19, UK

Motto: There is a way...
the mothers!

Goethe (Faust II)

Contents:

Foreword

Over the last few years the families of cerebrally palsied children have become tantalisingly aware of a new hope for the mental and physical development of their children, Conductive Education. They are also aware that for most of them this hope must be a distant one - in all probability too distant to benefit their own children.

The Foundation for Conductive Education, a national charity, was created to "establish the science and skill of Conductive Education in the United Kingdom" and plans to create a National Institute. Other organisations are also now working to bring Conductive Education out of Hungary, not only to these shores but to other lands too, but it is bitterly clear that it will be a very long time, if ever, before everyone who might potentially benefit from this approach can have access to services like those developed in Hungary.

Every year around one in every five hundred children born join the numbers of those with cerebral palsy. Demand is immense. A small number of families will travel to Budapest to attend the Petö Institute but most of their children will be relatively well on into their development and pressure of numbers means that they will receive at best only occasional four- to six-week visits. A growing number of families will also benefit from more extensive Conductive experience in those schools and units in this country which are now employing their own conductors from Hungary but again the numbers of children involved comprises but a tiny proportion of those who might potentially benefit. It remains to be seen how broad and extensive will be the Conductive Education that they experience.

Many more children will find their present special schools offering "principles of Conductive Education". Large numbers of professionals, teachers and therapists have now been to Budapest to observe the work at the Petö Institute. The quality and depth of their observations of course vary and the written scholarship on Conductive Education in the English language is still at an early stage of development. Despite the good intentions and hard work of everyone involved, therefore, we are only at the beginning of creating effective movement education systems in our special schools.

Parents do not expect miracles. They want an educational approach to their children's disability, one that sets out determinedly and confidently to transform their children's dysfunctional development. A transformational education has three essential requirements, a philosophical approach that sees children's development as very much the product of their upbringing and education, methods appropriate to achieve this and the organisation whereby all this can be implemented. At kindergarten (nursery) and more so at school age these three demand a highly complex system, with theory, methods and organisation often quite different from those commonly met in our schools. This is why the training of conductors and the establishment of Conductive Education in new contexts is such a difficult and complicated task.

In the first two or three years of life, however. it may prove less tricky to find some of the ingredients for a successful transformation of the course of cerebrally palsied children's development. Many, many parents are already philosophically primed to the notion that their children's development depends upon the quality and nature of parental care, upbringing and education. They desperately <u>want</u> to affect the course of their children's development. And for the great majority of children in our society the essential organisational structure is already in place in the parent-child dyad (usually, of course, the mother-child dyad) that is the basic unit of all human social and personal development. In some fortunate situations the required methods seem to be created spontaneously out of the talents, resources and experiences of the family itself but in most cases parents desperately seek guidance on appropriate methods to observe, understand and guide their children. They want to know <u>what</u> <u>to</u> <u>do</u>.

This book by Károly and Magda Akos provides the parents of young cerebrally palsied children a most welcome window on the part of the practical and theoretical approaches of Conductive Education for a specific age group and context. It cannot provide the full panoply of the system. It is neither do-it-yourself kit nor panacea but, from a different wing of András Petö's intellectual heritage, it offers practical insight into a way of transforming young children's development through education, in which many parents may find the inspiration and reassurance that they have been seeking.

Professionals reading this book, whatever their discipline, will also find fascinating windows opened, some expectations confirmed and perhaps some refuted too. Some may find the Central European style and vocabulary unfamiliar but it would have been unfair to the original to tamper excessively for fear of losing its flavour. "Gymnastics" seems commonly used in Hungary with the sense of exercises rather than the more formal activities implied by the word in English. The words "heal" and "healer" do not necessarily imply to cure but in an older, less technical sense to make whole.

Though terminology differs, underlying concepts may be comfortingly familiar. "Anthropogenic cooperation" refers to the interactions, the reciprocity, out of which human personality develops, with the child playing an active role. Dysfunction is seen as a learned, psychological outcome of disability within this context, with "metamorphosis", transformation, possible through appropriate adult attention. Movement is not some separate, physical product of nerves and muscles, but arises essentially out of the joint, meaningful activity of adult and child, within the emotional bond of parent and child.

Most especially the developmental psychology described evokes the work of Vygotskii and his followers. Their stages of development, early age (which is the central concern of this book) in which children learn best acting on their world in close emotional bond with their parents, kindergarten age in which the leading role is taken by collaborative and symbolic play with peers, and then on to school age with its more formal instruction - close parallels are apparent in this book.

Naive interpretations by visitors to Budapest, seeking to ground what they have seen or heard there firmly within the framework of existing practice and structures, have suggested that Conductive Education is somehow a mix, combination or agglutination of teacher, therapist, nurse etc. Both the practical accounts and the theoretical statements given here by Károly and Magda Akos confirm the necessity to take on the child's total psychological development, not least its emotional and motivational aspects, in any attempt to create movement education for cerebrally palsied children.

This is a humane and compassionate book respecting the autonomy of parents. It recognises how isolated they may feel in bringing up a cerebrally palsied child and how existing services can appear alienating and incomprehending. It offers no magic solution to all their problems but reassurance of what can be achieved by love and intelligent observation, patience and persistence. The help and supervision of an experienced conductor might be of enormously more benefit than this book can offer - but for most this is not available. Short of that, whatever the occasional disagreements, parents should not cut themselves off from or cease to fight for the specialised help the existing system provides. Perhaps this book will help better articulate what additional help it is that they seek.

Károly and Magda Akos hoped that their book would enable parents to band together to help each other. At the time of writing, this hope has not been realised in the German Federal Republic where *Dina* was first published. Perhaps in the English-speaking world, with its strong traditions of self-help and parental organisation, the Akoses' hope might prove more readily realisable.

Andrew Sutton
May 1991

Preface

This book is dedicated to Dina, a severely disabled German girl. Essentially it is a documentation of the correspondence between her mother and ourselves. When we heard about Dina for the first time, we had no idea how important the experience would be for us. It looks as if this chance meeting could transform the fate of children with cerebrally caused motor disorder. Therefore this book, which reports the change in Dina, rightfully bears her name. It is intended for mothers of infants and small children with brain damage (cerebral palsy), for those mothers who are deprived of the "wonderful" ability which all mothers have to promote the development of their child's personality. Yet it is exactly this ability which enabled these mothers to learn how to help their physically and mentally handicapped children.

In the social reality of the German Federal Republic, as in almost any other country, it is the mother who is normally responsible for the education of the children. This is especially true with disabled children, which is the reason why this book is directed at mothers. This does not mean that it is only the natural mother who has this special ability which is so important for children's personality development. For mother one may substitute the father or any other person to whom the child relates closely.

This book uses a very small number of specialist terms like "physically handicapped", "cerebral disorder", "cerebral palsy", which the reader may also find in other literature in this field. The definitions of these terms are still debated by specialists. We think that the term should be "cerebral dysfunction", which is explained in the textbook by Hári and Akos "Conductive Education" as follows:

"An orthofunctional person is characterized by a general capacity for adaptation or learning which enables him throughout his life to adjust more and more comprehensively to his natural

1

and social environment, and on that general capacity his life-long development depends.

But the general adaptive capacity of dysfunctional people is diminished or has been lost altogether, so that they are incapable in many ways of achieving the adaptation expected of them. They cannot learn to adapt to new circumstances."

Conductive Education strives to restore the missing "orthofunction". This helps to overcome the dysfunction and the individual will gradually be socialized. Accordingly, from the very start, daily activities are adapted to the "normal way of living" of the child's age group.

While medical specialists, general, special and remedial educationalists, and other professionals dispute their respective areas of competence in cerebral dysfunction, it must be stated clearly that Conductive Education cannot be assigned to one area and does not represent a mixture of disciplines. It embodies a special way of applying "anthropogenic cooperation"[1] to people with cerebral dysfunction and educating them towards orthofunction.

As for "anthropogenic cooperation" we wish only to mention here that the influence of an intercerebral relationship (between two or more brains) is necessary for the development of the human ability for adaptation. The first phase of this development occurs between the baby and his mother. This is the beginning of the child's personality development. Further development of the personality is determined by a variety of anthropogenic cooperations (K. Akos and M. Akos: *The Meaning of Human Life - Relational Psychology*).

Therefore what the infant needs is not treatment to overcome his dysfunction: instead his mother needs competent help to enable her to establish anthropogenic cooperation with the infant

1   Some of the terms used by Akos and Akos may be unfamiliar to English readers, but where they have been retained they are explained by the authors.

in spite of the difficulties resulting from the brain damage. That way the infant can catch up with normal development.

Here the authors wish to thank the mothers of Dina and Steffi, both for the permission for quoting the letters and for their numerous valuable initiatives and important comments. We wish also to thank Frau Galla for translating our letters.

For simplicity we generally use the pronoun "he" when referring to children in this book.

The book

This book consists of two parts. The first part ("a booklet for mothers") consists of the slightly modified booklet which resulted from our work with Dina and was intended in 1986 as a support for other mothers. This booklet demonstrates how a mother can help her child through Conductive Education.

The second part is a chronological account of the development of Dina and Steffi, documented by the letters between the mothers, Frau Galla and ourselves.

Explanations and remarks inserted into the text by the authors are in italics.

Names have been changed.

Part I: A booklet for mothers

By "mother", we mean not only the natural mother but also any person in close contact with the child. This can be the father, grandmother or an uncle. In most cases, however, it is the natural mother and therefore we will refer to her.

What can a mother do to overcome the cerebral dysfunction of her infant or small child?

1. What does "cerebral dysfunction" mean and how can it be overcome?

A child is born. The mother is happy that everything is all right. Full of hope she watches her infant's development. Everything is quite normal, she has enough milk, the infant feeds well and puts on weight. But sometimes, especially if this is not her first child and she already has experience of child rearing, she realizes that something is wrong. She goes to see a doctor and sooner or later is told that her child is handicapped. This is a very difficult time.

What follows is total subjection to the advice of various specialists, physiotherapists, therapists and special educators, who back up their treatments by countless test results and irrefutable theories from experts. Exercises must be performed, appliances used, operations carried out.

The specialists think the results are acceptable but the mother is not happy. She compares her child with other children of the same age and thinks that he still behaves differently.

She is told to be patient and is given vague information about structural details of the brain.

Time passes and the mother can see that her child is getting worse and worse compared with other children of the same age. She may even be advised to look for a place in a home where the child can live in good conditions and where all his needs are cared for. Why should a mother accept this?

Mothers prefer to follow the advice of specialists who are not "over-optimistic" but who make almost unrealistic demands of them, if this gives them something to hope for.

The authors of this book hold a different view.

We want to encourage mothers to realize their natural ability, the natural ability of the human species, and to develop courage and perseverance in using it. The human species survives not only by having sufficient offspring but also by mothers creating independent and cooperative personalities. The basis of this is established in that very important initial period after birth. The mother is not usually conscious of her ability. Not only does she create the necessary conditions for bringing up a baby, without being aware of the details of what she is doing, but also she does not realize that she is promoting her infant's personality development. For a handicapped child, however, it is extremely important that the mother becomes aware of her ability to initiate the child's personality development.

A mother who understands this can, with support and with relatively little instruction, overcome the baby's interrupted personality growth and also reduce the symptoms of movement disorder. Instruction is necessary because the relationship between mother and infant which normally exists is reduced or prevented by the child's brain damage.

The mother has to be shown that she can develop her child's abilities and that as a consequence his symptoms will diminish. The most difficult thing is making mothers aware of their abilities despite the often discouraging opinions of many rival specialists.

We do not expect mothers of handicapped infants and small children to trust our viewpoint from the outset. On the contrary, we want to encourage mothers to trust their own experience, and to do so critically. Their own wishes and fears should always be set against their own experience and judged again.

We learned about healing handicapped children from the work of the Hungarian physician András Petö (1893-1967). By applying "Conductive Education", he was able to help thousands of handicapped children in his Institute. (By real help we mean that the child does not differ in ability from other children of the same age, that is, he is healed.) We have also found that mothers can learn to use the Petö System for infants and small children who, because of their age, cannot be separated and live in the Petö Institute. We realized that mothers can use the Petö System so that their handicapped child can be completely healed in a very short time, at a very early age.

With this booklet we want to enable mothers of cerebral handicapped children to recognize the symptoms of this brain damage at an early stage and to be able to contribute to the child's complete mental and physical health by using the Petö System. We want to support mothers in developing their nearly miraculous ability so that they can begin healing their handicapped children.

However, this requires the mother to recognize the cerebral dysfunction of her child as early as possible.

2. How can cerebral dysfunction be recognized early?

It is generally supposed that motor disorders, classified according to various symptoms under different terms, are caused by irreparable damage to the brain. Scientists debate the symptoms and their cerebral origin. However, this does not interest the mother. She wants to know how she can heal her child. This wish can be fulfilled since functional disorders caused by damage to the brain structure can be compensated. This compensation can be achieved through appropriate cooperation between mother and child. The sooner motor disturbances are recognized and adequate treatment begun, the better and faster the compensation.

The mother recognizes a motor disturbance not with the help of tests of reflexes but by her impression that something is not the way that it should be.

In the early stages this deviation from normality can easily be overlooked as it is not always conspicuous.

The thumb, for example, can be pressed toward the palm, under the other fingers. When we take a close look, we often see that the fingers are not in line, sometimes they even lie over each other. When we try to move the infant's arms we find that they are bowed and pressed to the body. At the same time the hands form fists and the wrist is bent towards the palm. These symptoms can occur simultaneously, singly, on one or on both sides. They may intensify temporarily, especially when the infant is frightened by something unexpected. This happens for example when he is put into water too quickly, or when there is too much water in the bath so that the child floats. In the early stages these symptoms may occur only in exceptional situations such as these.

Non-handicapped babies have their arms at right angles to the body when they sleep, the elbows are bent, the hands form fists but the thumbs are on the outside and the wrist is bent towards the back of the hand. When the baby is awake he moves his hands and arms continuously and vigorously. A handicapped child, however, moves his arms and hands only a little or not at all.

A healthy newborn baby lies relaxed on the back, knees bent and open, feet bent upwards. He often kicks his feet energetically. The handicapped baby in comparison is always in a resting position.

When he is laid on the back his legs are often asymmetrical. Sometimes they are fully extended, sometimes they are crossed. From time to time one leg lies on the other, turned to the inside. The ankle is often extended too. The infant does not thrash about. When he is held up vertically, the legs do not move, they are extended, sometimes crossed, and the feet are also extended.

The asymmetrical posture of the body can be another important sign of motor disorder. Tensions in parts or the whole of the musculature can also occur (the scientific terms are "spasm" or "rigidity"). Because of the tense muscular system certain postures ("contractures") can only be changed with great effort.

The healthy infant lying naked on his back does not remain still but makes winding movements with the trunk and thrashes about with his arms and legs. Quite often an infant of three or four weeks with bent knees presses his heels against his nappy, then extends the legs and tenses the body with such force that the nappy slips off. This will never happen with handicapped children. They are conspicuously quiet.

A healthy baby cries loudly when he does not feel well and so draws the mother's attention to himself. A handicapped child can be so hindered by his muscular tension that he only whimpers quietly (and the parents are glad that they have such a good child).

The behaviour of a healthy child can change remarkably quickly while that of a handicapped child remains nearly or totally the same. It is normal that a newborn child raises his open hands up to the side of the head when there is an unexpected, frightening sound ("The Moro reflex"). A motor disorder, however, is signalled by this reflex lasting for months or even years, often in a very strong form.

Sometimes too the head bends backwards and the legs are overstretched ("Opisthotonus"). In this posture the arms are bent at the elbows, the wrists towards the palm. The thumbs are pressed into the palm by the fingers. The whole body is immovable and rigid. This posture cannot be changed by force. If the mother then takes the child on her lap, caresses him or puts him into bed and talks quietly with him, if she strokes and soothes him, he will regain his trust and the symptoms will vanish or at least diminish.

The early symptoms of a newborn handicapped child are often thought to be exaggerated reactions. This means that the mother may not recognize them as motor disorders. The mother may think that this is a game which her child loves to play. She does not get alarmed until the child is still unable to lift his head at the age of three or four months. This shows her that something is seriously wrong with her child. Now she hears for the first time the different terms that the physicians use for different forms of motor disorder ("Monoplegia, Paraplegia, Hemiplegia, Tetraplegia", and so on) and she hears strange explanations about dead brain cells. Not only does the mother get frightened, she also feels desperate, without hope and passive. She loses faith in her child's future. She hears about other motor-disordered children who are still at the level of an infant as adults, unable to eat or speak and needing constant help in daily life. Is that the prospect for her own child?

The infant is endangered both by the mother's hopelessness and by the wrong impression that he gives of being a "good" child. His mother may be happy that he does not demand as much attention as his brothers and sisters at the same age. Involuntarily she neglects him, although he needs more care than his brothers and sisters. And so his passivity turns into apathy.

In reality the child has brain damage which prevents him from attracting his mother's attention by incessantly changing his behaviour. Yet attention is essential. For example, a healthy child triggers in his mother a desire to play with him. He influences this play by his behaviour. The mother is mostly unaware that she is led by the child in this way; this happens unconsciously.

Many specialists also still either underestimate the importance of cooperation between child and mother in play for the child's personality development, or are not clear about it. It is known that playing absorbs more and more of the mother and child's time and that both enjoy it. The mother of a handicapped child is uncertain and self-conscious because of the symptoms of brain damage, and this results in her increasing neglect of the child's personality development, which finally can lead to total apathy.

With appropriate instruction the mother of a motor-disordered child should be able to do the same things with her child as can the mother of a healthy child. This is the only way to heal a motor-disabled child, for he learns to compensate for his symptoms and his behaviour becomes "normal".

Here we want to mention a question that will most certainly arise. What would happen if a mother treated her totally healthy child like a handicapped one because she misinterpreted things? The answer is simple: nothing!

There is no essential difference between the mother's necessary behaviour in both cases, only that with a healthy child a mother will "instinctively" behave correctly, while with a handicapped child she has to be made aware of the appropriate behaviour, by means of suitable instruction. Without this instruction she will unconciously neglect the mother-child cooperation necessary for the physical and mental development of a handicapped child.

The only reason that a healthy child develops is that his mother often plays with him and so channels his activities in the right way.

3. What should a mother do with a cerebrally damaged child?

The infant's development cannot be accelerated. But it is possible, even necessary, for the mother to take notice of her infant's inclinations and not to ignore his dislikes when solving current problems. The child achieves his aims. He gets what he wants and he enjoys that.

This does not mean that the mother has to give up her goals and their realization. On the contrary, the child's personality development is promoted by the mother's ability to avoid what the child dislikes and to do things that the child enjoys.

An infant has fun only when he strives actively for something, that is when motivated and able to reach his desired goal. This can be seen best when the child plays.

As often as possible a mother of a handicapped child should take the initiative to play with her child, if he is not asleep or ill.

She awakens his motivation. With her help the child achieves his goals. If she is good at it, the child's activity increases, his attention intensifies, he is happier and cooperates more and more with his mother.

When the child begins to be tired and passive and his attention decreases, play should not just be repeated but be made interesting and new by little modifications, so that the child takes part actively again. When an infant sleeps, of course, he must not be awakened to play.

The mother of a handicapped child must be totally aware of what play means for herself and for the child and what she wants to achieve by it. This is the only way to understand which games should be played and in which way they can or should be played.

Now we want to show how the mother can play with her infant.

How can she play at all if the infant's legs are in the "unusual" posture described above?

The child lies on his back on a hard surface. The mother pushes both feet slowly (!) towards his bottom. She has to take care that the heels and soles of the feet are flat on the surface. Now the lower legs are in a vertical position, the knees point upwards. The mother does this while saying repeatedly: " I pull up my feet".

She keeps the feet in this position for a short time, sings a song or recites a rhyme and talks to the child. This way the child's attention is drawn to the activity.

Later she can vary this; for example she may take the infant's feet, bend them upward and knock the heels softly on the surface while saying a rhyme in a slow rhythm, for example, "Knock, knock, steady like a clock", or something similar.

You can see clearly from the child's behaviour that he likes the game. The infant has achieved his goal: his mother plays with him.

But what is the mother's goal? She wants to teach the child to bend his knees and to keep his heels on the ground. The child learns these movements gradually when playing. After some time, when he is able to stay in this position without his mother's help, firstly for a short time, later for longer, she can see that he has actually learned the movements. When the legs stretch out again, she says: "This is fine, stretch your legs nicely".

So the infant learns when his legs are bent and the feet are flat on the surface and when his legs are extended.

This playful teaching can be developed further by the age of 1 - 2 months:

The child lies flat on a base, legs bent, feet close to his bottom. The mother presses the heels slightly to the base, bends the feet gently upwards and puts light pressure on the knees. This way she achieves stretching of the legs. Because she keeps the heels on the base, the child glides backwards. She says while doing so: "We drive along, drive along on a big red bus" and the like.

The child enjoys playing this and wants to do it again.

What can he learn by doing this? The mother realizes after a certain time that the child bends his knees all by himself, puts his feet on the ground, presses the heels on the surface and pushes himself backwards. So this play has helped the infant to learn a form of independent mobility with his legs. Originally he was unable to do so because of the spastic extension of the legs and the overstretching of the feet. He has now learned to suppress these symptoms, at least temporarily, when lying on his back and playing.

Another example: The mother starts to integrate grasping into the game described above.

To learn to grasp something is the most important factor in the learning process of motor-disordered children. At first it seems superfluous to teach an infant to grasp something, as every newborn child seizes the things that touch his palms. (This is called the "gripping response".) Motor-disordered children often have their hands in a fist which they cannot open spontaneously since the gripping response is triggered by their own fingers. The gripping response is very strong and, like the Moro reflex, is apparent for many months. As voluntary opening or closing of the hands is not possible, it is also impossible to learn to grip and develop further from this.

To teach her two-month-old infant to grasp something, the mother can play the following:

She puts the infant on his back and her forefinger into his carefully opened hand. The child grasps it because of the gripping response. It may be necessary to correct the position of the fingers so that they are then lying next to each other, not one above the other. The thumb has to be opposite the fingers. This is the correct grip. She puts her thumb on the infant's fingers so that they do not move. Then she supports his wrist with the middle finger so that the gripping hand does not bend downwards, towards the palm, but a little upwards. This is the natural position of a gripping hand.

The mother accompanies all this with words, saying what she and the child are doing - like a story-teller.

Now the actual game can begin. The mother recites or sings a song or a rhyme, for example "Pat-a-cake, pat-a-cake, baker's man", and brings the little fists together and apart again. After repeating it several times she stretches the child's arms wide apart and says something like: "Such...a big cake we bake".

This teaches the child not only to grip but also to stretch his arms.

For the child these are not exercises but a game. You can easily see how much he likes it. He will not only like this game but also show by his behaviour that he wants it repeated. This way the child is motivated to play, the game becomes his goal.

You can play with handicapped children as well as with healthy ones. But it is more difficult to create the conditions for play needed by a handicapped child.

Thanks to the mother's goal of education, the child has not only learned the right position for his fingers and wrists in the game described above but has also experienced relief from the pressure of tense upper arms on his chest.

The child will learn what he has achieved actively and joyfully in play. Success thus achieved can be developed further, for example, towards grasping a rattle.

A rattle is a well-known toy that needs no further explanation. At first, however, a motor-disordered child has to have a special rattle, one which he can grasp properly. It must be like a dumb-bell with a straight handle, long enough for the fingers to grasp, as described above. The most important thing here is that the thumb lies opposite the fingers. The mother has to control the position of the fingers with care and correct it if necessary. The handle should be about the same size as the mother's forefinger, which the infant can already grasp. At first she may have to support the wrist with her own middle finger. She may also have to grasp gently the infant's gripping hand so that the infant does not let go of the rattle. Now they move the rattle and the mother sings a little song or recites a rhythmical nursery rhyme. This seems an interesting game, from which the child learns a lot. The mother can see this when the infant is able to hold the rattle by himself. After a certain time he will correct a wrong position of the fingers or the hand by himself if the mother tells him to do so.

Here we have to make an additional remark about the precise way in which a statement must be formulated.

The sentence "The infant has the rattle in his hand" contains very general information. It is important to watch the details of how the child holds the rattle.

When lying on his back a motor-disordered infant may be able to hold a rattle in his right hand but not in his left hand. Or he may be able to hold it in one hand when lying on his back but not when sitting up or lying on his front. You may easily get the impression that the child does not understand what is expected, even though he should be able to do so, as he has already learned it.

Now the mother has to realize where the concrete problem lies and how it can be solved, so that her infant can hold the rattle. She must realize that even though it is called the same, "gripping" is something different for the left hand than for the right or when the infant is in different positions. This difference also exists in the learning process of healthy children, although with them it is not so conspicuous as they learn much faster.

It is different with a handicapped child whose learning ability is disturbed. The mother can help her child if she adapts her educational support to her child's special problems. She should know, for example, that if her infant has learned to hold a rattle in a certain position, this does not mean that he is able to do so in any other position. If the child does not understand what his mother wants him to do, she has to look patiently for ways in which this problem might be solved. The question of how to solve problems in different situations will come up again and again.

Now we go on with the game.

What are the possibilities for further development if the infant has already learned to grip a rattle?

The infant can take the rattle and hold it by himself. He can now shake it on his own as he did before with his mother's help. He can also let go of the rattle - a big step forward as the gripping response can now be stopped at will. The child can hold the rattle, let it go and the mother can hand it back. An infant likes this game and his mother realizes that he has not only learned to grip but also to let go. Now she can go on teaching the child to grasp things that lie in front of him, without help. But this is only possible if the child has already learned to open his hand.

It is important to pay attention to symmetry when a child learns to grip. For this the mother can give the infant two rattles, one for each hand. If one hand is more clumsy than the other, the mother gives the rattle to this hand. The child's hands, however, must never be called the "good" and the "clumsy" hand, but always the right and the left hand. After a certain time the child will grasp with the right or the left hand, according to what his mother tells him.

As soon as the infant can grasp, hold and let go of the rattle, the mother gives him other toys for similar use. For example, from the start, children should have a nice colourful, soft cloth about the size of a handkerchief, which they first grasp by chance, then later on purpose, and which they can shake and look at carefully. (It is advisable to have several of them as substitutes, since many children take it with them into bed for years and do not want to to be without it even when it needs washing.) The child gains experience by grasping toys of different shape, colour, size, texture, solidity and so on. He learns to play on his own for longer and longer periods. The mother can enjoy watching her baby playing independently and thus has more time for other things.

The mother of a handicapped child must be aware of how important playing is for learning.

4. What does the child learn from independent play?

When an infant holds toys and shakes them, he learns how to solve complex problems. While he happily grasps a rattle, shakes it, lets it go, picks it up and puts it down again, his brain combines very varied items of sensory perception and signals for movement. When an infant has something in his hand, brings it before his eyes, turns it and puts it down again, this combines visual, tactile and auditory sensations with movement. This supports the development of understanding shapes, recognizing objects visually and auditorily at different distances and in different positions, in short, the interaction of very varied items of sensory perception and differentiation between them.

While an infant grasps and moves things, moving the fingers, bending the wrist, turning the arms, bending and stretching become an "activity", an expression of complex brain functions, organised in space and time. When he grasps toys and puts them to his mouth, specialists talk about "hand-eye-mouth-co-ordination". This is not normally important for a mother. For her it is important that her infant, when able to play with different things, can grasp these and put them in his mouth, that he can hold a glass and help with the spoon. This makes an infant increasingly independent. The mother realizes that playing makes her child more and more skilful. The games can always be developed a bit further and the mother becomes happy at the growing dexterity of her child.

Playing creates the conditions for later developments not yet perceptible. When, for example, an infant plays with a piece of crust, he puts it in his mouth, licks it, tastes it, and rubs it against his gums. This is not only a preparation for chewing but also for the movement of the lips, the cheeks, the jaws and the tongue, all necessary for speaking. Children only learn to speak when they are able to chew.

We would never advise giving a dummy to a healthy child. However, it seems advisable to give one to a handicapped child of about four or five months if he is incapable of putting toys into his mouth. When he is teething he can rub his gums with it. The child closes his mouth around the dummy and turns it around with his tongue. To initiate turning the tongue, you can put the dummy into the mouth the wrong way round. This creates the conditions for chewing and later on for active speaking. The dummy should of course be put into the mouth by the child's hand with the mother's help (hand-eye-mouth-coordination). This is not to be confused with drinking from a bottle with a teat, which is wrong in any circumstances.

So the child plays with various things that he can grasp. Through this play he gains biologically important experience. He plays with a colourful piece of cloth, then with a rattle, later - especially when he gets his teeth - with a piece of crust or something hard with which he can rub his gums. The favourite games change from time to time, so does the way of playing. The child learns through all play and he also learns to play independently. But the precondition for this is regular cooperation with his mother. She plays with the child and gives him the things he needs to play independently. The mother takes part in the child's games in various ways to make the child more independent - independent also in the way he interacts with her. In this way learning in a general-biological sense takes on a human-biological quality.

How does the mother know what to do with her infant?

5. The mother's role in the child's process of learning.

The mothers of two-month-old and six-month-old infants play differently with their children. Essentially each learns how to play from the child himself. Even a young baby shows the mother whether he likes a game. Not only is a mother directed by her own child but also by the experience she gains from other children of the same age. Mothers always watch the behaviour of other mothers and children, draw comparisons and gather ideas for the education of their own child. They know their own child's peculiarities quite well but always compare his achievements with others. This is how the mother recognises the motor disorder of her own child. A mother will be worried if her three- or four-month-old child cannot lift up his head when lying on his front, like other children of his age. If she watches her child closely she will realize that he does try to lift his head but does not succeed. These attempts at movement can serve as a starting point for the mother to teach her infant the right posture of the head. She does not want to hear scientific lectures about the tonus of individual muscles or about organizational defects of head control to explain why her baby does not lift his head as other babies do. But she is interested in how to teach her baby to lift and hold up his head.

This is possible as follows.

Healthy children do not lift their heads all the time when lying on their front. A healthy infant lifts his head if he wants to look at a person some distance away or at an object. Otherwise the head of a baby lying prone is turned to one side and he can only see what is happening on this side. A motor-disordered child wants to lift his head too, if something interesting is happening. But he cannot do so without help.

The mother puts a folded blanket under the infant's chest so that his body is raised a little. She puts his hands as flat as possible in front of the blanket so that the palms are on the floor. His elbows are bent. In this position, if he is curious - and only then - he can lift his head a little for just a short time. The mother then sits in front of the child, her face close to his head. She talks to the baby, calls him, sings or shows him toys. Motivated by this, the baby momentarily lifts his head up to body level. Now he can see more than before, which is exactly the mother's educational aim. Now the child starts to learn to lift his head. Further development is possible if the mother goes on finding ways of attracting her baby's attention for as long as possible. Later she teaches him to grasp toys that lie in his reach. This brings about stretching of the elbows. This way the child learns how to lift his head higher and higher and so see more and more things.   At first the arms may be stretched for just a short time, later for longer and longer periods. To maintain stretching a little bit longer the mother can initially support the extended elbows. She will soon see that the arms give way less often and that the head is kept so high that her child's big, admiring eyes never let her out of his sight, even if she does not bend down to him. When his head starts to drop she talks to the baby and tries to attract his attention again. This way he can keep his head up longer (the mother of course notices when the child gets tired and stops playing).

She will be pleased when she can take the blanket away from under the baby's chest, as he has learned to lift and keep his head up independently. She now has to think about how to attract his attention for an even longer time.

As soon as the child is able to support himself with outstretched arms and raised head, the mother gives him a toy in one hand or makes him drum the surface, first with one hand and then with the other. She teaches the baby to grasp something and finds after a while that he holds his head up while supporting himself with only one hand...

When playing, a child learns what he needs to develop his independence. His mother helps him to do so. Motor-disordered children learn in the same way but only when the mother is aware of her role in this educational process. When the child begins to learn to grasp, for example, she puts something in front of him so that he can easily grab it. At this stage she has to support the gripping and holding. She should then gradually diminish her support, form new, more difficult goals and thus motivate the child. For this there are various possibilities.

For example, a child lies on his front, his head raised. Obviously he is already tired; the elbows are still extended but they are about to give way. If the mother now lets one elbow buckle, the child falls to the side. She changes place, so she sits by his side. The child follows her with his eyes, which usually makes him turn his head towards his mother and roll on to his back. "You have rolled over, aren't you clever?", says the mother. This is how the child starts to learn how to change position. The same result can be achieved if the mother encourages her child to grasp a toy with stretched arms. She has to hold it in such a way that the child turns on his side when trying to grab it and rolls on to his back.

Solving such little tasks fosters learning, which is the basis for the development of the child's personality development. In this learning process the mother, through her educational activities, plays the fundamental role. The importance of the individual parts and steps of this educational activity is clear only to the mother of a dysfunctional child. They can therefore be used consciously.

The mother can teach her child to roll from his back on to his front as follows.

First she teaches him to turn on his side. She stands at the child's side when he is lying on his back and attracts his attention by talking to him. He wants to see his mother and turns a little bit to one side. Then she offers him a finger or a toy (for this the child must learn to grip). He tries to reach the target with the upper hand and stretches his arm. Sometimes this causes the baby to turn on to his front. If this does not happen, however, the mother has to look carefully for the reason and think about how she could help the child to overcome this problem on his own. In this way this movement will be learned as an activity.

One thing that she has to watch is that the other arm does not get stuck under the trunk. So she makes the baby, who is still lying on his back, stretch his arms above his head. If the child now grips one of his mother's fingers and turns over with her help, he ends up lying on his tummy, propped up on one elbow and his lower arm. With his mother's help the child can understand this movement.

By carefully watching her child the mother learns to find tasks that he likes and to help her child solve them. These tasks are partly initiated by the child himself and partly "copied" from other children.

The child also learns when playing on his own. But even then the mother creates the necessary conditions and tries to further his development. A handicapped child does not differ from other children in this respect but he has greater and more particular difficulties. That is why the mother faces greater and special demands in her educational work. Her task is to increase the child's activity, to observe the details of movements and formulate individual solutions to problems which are normally not considered. A mother can do that.

6. What can confuse the mother's observations?

Mothers are good "instinctive" observers of their children. Due to this the child's personality develops easily in most cases. The mother of a motor-disordered child, however, faces unexpected difficulties in the upbringing of her child. It is therefore understandable that she asks specialists for advice.

She may hear that her child is motor-disordered and therefore not able to follow the usual path of human development. This now has to be done. The child should first creep and then crawl. (This theory does not sound bad. Our ancestors, however, were not sealions, they neither crept nor crawled. Maybe some of the specialists were playing truant when that was explained at school.) It may happen that when crawling the arms give way and the child falls forward. The crawling programme can therefore not be applied. The mother is told that the baby has weak arms and the muscles have to be strengthened. However, this is not possible. So what can be done?

The mother must clearly understand her child's real situation. For this it is necessary to rid herself of such wrong ideas and theories and to pay attention to her child, not to some ancient ancestors. Instead of asking other people why her baby's arms bend when he is crawling, she should rely on her own observation. Do the elbows bend because the muscles are too weak? The mother can try to extend the arms. In most cases she will find that there is strong resistance preventing the elbows from stretching (this must not be tried with force). It is not weight that makes the arms bend, because the muscles are too weak, but an extraordinary physical force, the "spasm". It may happen that this bending spasm of the arms disappears in a lying or sitting position but not in the crawling position. It is possible that the weight of the body plays a role here as well, not because of the supposed weakness of the muscles but because of the increase of the spasm in this position.

Her activity with her child must therefore be based not on abstract, schematic ideas but on her own experience and observations.

However, certain false ideas may hinder the mother in doing this. For example she may hear that the usual developmental path must be followed, or that gross movements have to be learned before fine ones and so on.

A mother should watch her child without prejudices and look for ways to support real development. In this way she finds out that her child aquires abilities, for example, by gripping different things in various positions, which superficially have nothing to do with each other. But as long as a motor-disordered child is unable to use his hands, in other words does not learn to grip, he can hardly learn anything else.

In the above-mentioned task the child learns how to bend and stretch his arms deliberately in any position. In this way the spasm will disappear. But we will return to that later.

The innumerable experiences given by visual, tactile, and auditory perception, and also by the sense of taste and smell, are the basis for mental development; it is not (or only partially) possible to gain these experiences without the ability to grasp objects. The verb 'to grasp' has a dual meaning. Either one can grasp a concept or one can grasp an object. This is not just a linguistic coincidence, cognitive and motor experiences are inextricably bound together.

But it is not only certain ideas and theories which keep the mother from trusting her own experience and observation, it is also the fascination and the supposed omnipotence of technology. It is a misunderstanding to believe that new technology always surpasses the old, for simplicity is not always surpassed by complexity. This attitude can lead to the mother not recognizing the most effective educational equipment.

7. The Petö System's equipment and its uses.

The correct equipment has to be used for educating motor-disordered children to overcome their specific difficulties, but this does not mean complicated equipment. A marvellous piece of apparatus that we have already encountered is the rattle. We have shown how varied its use is if the right type is carefully chosen.

It is not only toys that are useful for learning but also items of daily use, for example a mug. A mug is very useful for training and developing gripping. One must, however, think about how to use a mug and what sort of a mug is to be used.

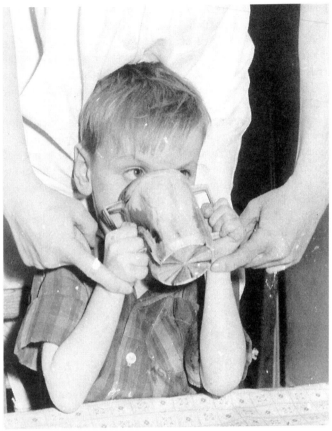

This photo from the book *Conductive Education* by Hári and Akos shows a boy drinking from a two-handled mug.

The condition for learning is the child's activity, his striving for a goal, his motivation and satisfaction. A child should not learn to hold a mug when not thirsty, nor when the mug is empty. When a child cries, his mother first thinks that he is thirsty and gives him something to drink. To quench his thirst is an important opportunity for the mother to teach the child to grasp and hold a mug.

For this purpose we use to begin with a light plastic mug with two handles, which is only half filled. It should be light so that the child does not have to lift something too heavy. But why a mug with two handles? Not only because the child has more strength using two hands than one, but also to correct the cerebrally damaged child's tendency to asymmetric movement and posture. When learning to grip, the mother takes care that the fingers lie next to each other, the thumb is opposite them and the wrists are bent back. At first it may be that the mother has to hold the grasping hands with her own. But this is only possible if the handles are big enough; that means they have to reach from the bottom to the top of the mug.

As soon as the child can drink from a two-handled mug alone, he is allowed to drink from a "normal"one, a mug without handles. However, children with pronounced asymmetry of both halves of the body should drink from a two-handled mug for an even longer time. If a child insists on drinking from the same glass as the rest of the family but is yet unable to hold it, he can be given a mug with just one handle. This is explained to the child. In this case one has to take care that he uses both hands alternately. When eating with a spoon also take care that the spoon is held once in the right and once in the left hand. (One should have a spoon for the right and one for the left hand.) This makes it easier to switch a spoon from one hand to the other later on.

We have explained already that there is a wide range of different equipment for dysfunctional children, which has to be chosen carefully with regard to the level of development the child has already achieved.

Petö, the founder of Conductive Education, has given us excellent examples of equipment. Although they are technically quite simple, their potential is astonishing.

Let us take, for example, the wooden plinth. This seems to be a quite ordinary bed made of light springy oak or beech, indicating it has been carefully chosen. Its surface consists of smooth, varnished slats free of splinters and with rounded edges. The plinth is very light so it can be stood upright easily to create more space. It cannot fall down when stood on end, not even when a child clings to it. The surface is made of slats so that a hand can pass easily through the gaps to grip. Equipped with a mattress, blanket and sheets, it is an ideal and versatile bed.

But now let us discuss the teaching of gripping. With the child lying on his front, elbows bent, the mother makes him grip the slats. Now the child moves backwards a little to stretch his arms. In this way he learns to grip and to stretch his elbows while lying prone. At the same time the mother tells her child which hand he is using.

The bending spasm is stopped by learning to stretch the arms. This is an educational goal too.

The child's goal, however, is to slide backwards. Stretching and bending the arms is just part of a movement which brings about a "voluntary" change of position, that is, it is part of an activity.

The immediate motivation of the child may be a game. For example, he pretends that he is a car that reverses into a parking space, or an animal that walks backwards.

The same aim (stopping the bending spasm) is achieved by the child "voluntarily" stretching and bending his arms and thus moving forwards. On the plinth the child learns to grip a slat tightly and to move forwards. Take care that the child grips correctly. If not yet strong enough to pull himself forward, initially he must be helped by being pushed.

Motivation is always essential and indispensable. Here we have a lot of possibilities. For example, the mother puts a toy in front of the child so that by moving he can reach it easily. Then she encourages him to grasp it. Now he pulls himself forward a little. The mother can also sit at the top of the plinth and call the child to come towards her. Brothers and sisters can help with this and play as well.

At first the distance that the child can move on his front may be very short, but it will gradually increase. Meanwhile he can grip more strongly. The child has learned to change the position of the hands and to use gripping for bending and stretching the arms. The movement of the legs contributes to the pulling along and so the child learns coordination of hands and legs.

Next, the child learns to turn round on his front. For this his mother puts a teddy bear at his side and attracts his attention to it. When he moves towards the teddy, she moves it a little further away so that he moves further too. This way he learns to grip a slat with one hand to pull himself, and to push himself with the other, until he has turned around so that his head is now where the feet were.

If necessary the mother supports his grip by placing his fingers in the right position and helping to pull or push.

Both mother and child can sing a song or recite a nursery rhyme about a teddy bear, or something similar.

The child can also learn to turn when lying on his back. This is possible as follows.

The child is lying on his back and pulls himself with his right hand while pushing with the left one. At the same time he takes one "step" to the side with the left foot and follows with the right foot. This can also be done in the opposite direction, if the child is not tired. This way he not only learns to turn as a way of changing position, but also to take steps to one side or the other. He also learns to move the feet apart and to put them next to each other again, which is very difficult for children whose feet are spastically pressed together or crossed.

Simultaneously the mother talks to her child: " I put my left foot to the left side...I put my right foot next to it". Later the child can say that himself, so making the activities conscious.

However, this game is only important for a child if it is combined with other games or with the text of a song or of a rhythmical rhyme.

When the child has learned to grip the slat, this can be used for sliding down from the plinth. In this way the child reaches the ground with his feet and finally stands. (If the plinth is too high a platform can be put under his feet.) When he is learning to stand, he should touch the ground not just with his toes but also with the heels. The whole sole of the foot must stand flat on the ground. The mother also has to be careful to see that his knees are stretched, and if they are not she should support his knees with her hands. Later on she will see that the knees stay stretched while she moves her hands down his legs. Finally the child will no longer need support. However, until then the knees will often bend. This is not a matter of muscular strength since the child looks at his knees and stretches them when he is reminded of it.

The mother's praise for achieving his goals is extraordinarily important. The child will learn when he stands "perfectly straight". This may be accompanied by a song, for example: "I'm standing tall, just like a tree. My knees are straight as straight can be." This is a wonderful game for the child and a marvellous way for the mother to teach her child to stand for longer periods.

Now the mother can teach her child to sit. First he lies on his front, opens his legs a bit and pushes himself backwards. The mother stops his legs from sliding backwards. If his elbows do not yet stretch fully his mother can sit on the plinth to keep his legs in the right position and to support the stretching arms. In this way the child pushes himself backwards, the knees bend and head and trunk lift. Then a little chair is put on the plinth, with which he can pull himself up so that his trunk is even higher until he sits up straight. This can also be achieved with the child gripping his mother's fingers and so raising himself up to a sitting position.

The mother has already explained to her child that he is going to sit up and has accompanied each step with words. The child had no notion of what "to sit up" means; he has not learned it before he has actually sat up. He followed the instruction only for his mother's sake.

As soon as he sits there are so many new things to learn: to look out of the window, to look at a picture, to watch TV and so on.

When her child can sit, the mother thinks about how to teach him to maintain the sitting position and to avoid falling. Care must be taken that the child does not stay in this position for too long, but learns to change position.

Learning standing and sitting positions is an intermediate stage in the achievement of other educational aims. By gripping, the child learned to stand up by moving backwards. If the child is able to stand but still has to hold on to the plinth, his mother can develop these abilities and teach him to squat. Then he can sit on the potty. If this is done every two hours at first, and the child is praised when he has emptied bladder or bowels, he will soon be potty-trained.

So the plinth is not just a bed, but also an item with which gripping, sitting, crawling, standing and climbing can be learned.

As with the plinth, a simple chair is a piece of equipment with many varied uses. If motor-disordered children are put on a chair they may fall off easily. That is why they often wear a helmet or are fastened to the chair. These things are not just superfluous, they are wrong. A child wearing a helmet just learns that he can fall down without hurting his head. If he is fastened to the chair he will never learn to keep his balance.

However, the mother's aim is for her child to sit on a chair independently or to stand up and sit down as he wishes, and she can teach her child to do this. If he has already learned to grip, he should also be able to learn to maintain a sitting position and to support himself. To keep his balance can be achieved as follows.

The mother teaches her child to keep the soles and heels of his feet flat on the ground with his knees bent. Bending the knees keeps the trunk upright. If the chair is a bit too high, a

stool or a thick book can be put under his feet. The mother
shows him how to keep his feet flat on the ground and to sit

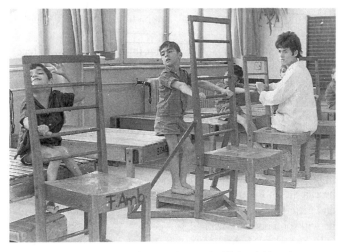

This photo from the book *Conductive Education* by Hàri and Akos shows
ladder-back chairs and plinths used in the Petö Institute.

correctly. He will not fall from the chair, if he sits "straight".
First the mother puts another chair with its back towards the
child. (This chair is called a ladder-back chair and has rungs all
the way up the back of it.) The child learns how to grasp these
rungs to sit safely. To keep the trunk straight, a rung at the appropriate height is gripped, the arms being extended horizontally. To keep him from falling to one side, his arms should be
wide apart. At first this can also be achieved by putting another
two chairs on either side of the child. This is better than using
an armchair, since its arms cannot be removed when the child
sits safely. As an intermediate stage, the mother may take away
one chair and stand at her child's side.

We have shown that the mother needs items that are very
simple but have various uses in the Petö System.

While the mother gradually realizes what measures are necessary for her child's learning and what she can do for his successful education, the practical alteration of the child's surroundings influence his personality development.

Meanwhile his mother will have discovered that more and more things can be used for her child's education.

8. Equipment for learning independence

A mother is continually confronted with her child's problems which have to be resolved, like the above example when the child was thirsty. She develops a natural readiness for recognizing and solving these problems. Motor disturbed children have special, additional problems. Solutions to these problems require methods comparable to those used to solve the problems of healthy children.

The child's personality development depends on the mother's educational activity, whether she is aware of it or not. By solving the child's current problems, a learning process that will lead to independence is set in motion. The mother of a healthy child contributes spontaneously to the process of personality development. However, if the child is motor-disordered the mother first has to learn how to help her child. She also has to learn that there are many ways to teach her child to be independent.

Activities that only serve the purpose of satisfying a child's needs, without asking for his cooperation, should be avoided in all circumstances. Instead his mother should look for ways of not only promoting the child's involvement, but also of widening it to include aspects of teaching and learning.

The apparatus that aids the evolution of independence has to be carefully considered, and for this constant observation of the child is indispensable. The best teaching equipment is that what can be disposed of after some time or that what allows a step-by-step reduction of the mother's support. In this way the learning process can develop gradually, as the level of achievement rises and independence increases.

In the above example, it was said that a child feels safer if, when sitting on a chair, there is a chair at each side to keep him from falling. Later on, first one, then the other chair is taken away, according to his ability to balance. Another way to support his ability to balance is to put him on a long bench. He may well fall to one side, but he can never fall down, and the mother can teach him to stay sitting if he supports himself with one hand. Later on it is enough for the mother to remind her child to sit straight to avoid falling: "I am sitting straight." This way she teaches her child to recognize the oblique position, to correct it and to develop a stable sense of balance.

Able-bodied children train their balance control when sitting by innumerable changes of position. This learning process takes place in a very short time and a conscious contribution from the mother is hardly necessary. The mother of a disabled child, however, has to realize how to develop this process step by step and to use the most simple and effective apparatus.

Consider the chair. A chair whose back consists of horizontal thin round rungs is best. It is helpful if the rungs also extend down between the back legs of the chair. The legs on each side have to rest on a slat so the chair can glide easily. It is made of light, smooth wood and has a smooth seat.

It is pointless to try to teach a healthy baby to sit until he is seven or eight months old. If he learns to sit by himself he should not be stopped. Instead one should observe the circumstances in which he sits with his back straight, to be able to recreate exactly those conditions. It is a difficult task to sit correctly, which is why many children learn to stand earlier than to sit if they have enough room and something they can grip. A motor-disordered child, however, will never learn to sit correctly if unable to move his arms freely and to grip. The child should not be taught to stand before the age of thirteen or fifteen months. Then he should be able to grip strongly and correctly and to stand upright.

But let us return to the ladder-back chair. A motor-disordered child can be taught to sit safely when sitting on a chair, a stool or a potty, by holding on to a ladder-back chair positioned in front of him. Here the child should grasp the rung which is at the same level as his shoulders, with both hands and with arms extended. His back should be straight. Curvature of the spine can be corrected when the child looks up to the mother's face or to some toy in her hand. If he still does not sit well, the position of his feet should be observed and, if necessary, corrected. When the sitting position is right, the mother tells and shows him that he is now sitting correctly.

With the help of the ladder-back chair the child has learned step by step how to stretch his arms. The mother may have had to put the rungs nearer to the child by tilting the chair so he could reach them by stretching his arms. As soon as the child is able to do this, the mother can put the chair slowly back into its original position so that his arms are totally extended. She accompanies this with: "I stretch my arms, I stretch, stretch...".

Sitting is made more and more difficult. First the child holds the chair with both hands, then only with one, and finally he should, just for a short time of course, sit without holding on to it. This way he learns to sit safely.

Such are the educational aims of the mother. The child accepts them most readily when they are integrated into games.

How can a ladder-back chair be used for learning to stand up?

The mother sits on a ladder-back chair the wrong way round, facing her child. The child sits on another chair and grasps a rung with extended arms. The mother encourages him to lean forward with his back straight and to grip the next higher rung with both hands in turn. Thus she teaches the child to "climb up" with his hands. The mother accompanies this with: "I reach higher with my left hand, I reach higher with my right hand..."; the child should join in, if possible. When necessary she reminds him to keep his arms stretched: "I stretch my arms". She also has to pay attention to his legs, which should be bent at the knees. If the posture is not right, the mother must correct it.

Finally she sees that he is now able to stand up and encourages him to do so if he wants to. She can support him with her hands and say: "I stand up". If necessary she stops her child's feet from slipping by putting her own feet in front of them. This way the child stands up.

By achieving this goal, the child learns gradually to set it for himself and to achieve it more and more independently. The aims that the child strives for are only understood and the actions that lead to it only learned by actually achieving the goal.

When the child needs to stand straight he is shown a picture on the ceiling or told to watch his hands clapping above the head, which makes him stand up straight. The mother tells him that he is now standing straight and he understands.

The above examples make clear what a simple but useful and multi-purpose teaching instrument the ladder-back chair is. It helps the child to achieve the intermediate stages essential for reaching goals. Later on the child can do without it. Good instructional equipment should offer the child the minimal necessary support for achieving a goal. The more one can do without support, the greater the independence.

When the child has succeeded in standing up, he still has to grasp the back of a chair for balance. The mother sits on the same chair, reversed, facing him to be able to keep him from falling and to support the gripping and stretching of his arms. Later on this support will become superfluous.

With older children, the ladder-back chair is stabilized by additional rungs, as can be seen on the picture in *Conductive Education* by Hári and Akos (p. 363).

The process of learning to stand begins with standing while holding on and is developed gradually to independent, unsupported standing. At first independent standing is not to be expected. After a relatively short time the child is able to take one hand away from the rung momentarily. To achieve this the mother gives him a little piece of cloth, for example, to wipe the rungs just as she does.

In this way she can make him accomplish through a game a task which he does not yet understand consciously or which he does not think he can do. Afterwards the mother tells the child that he has stood with just one hand gripping the chair. So the child becomes aware that he has learned to stand and to grip the chair with just one hand when "working".

To learn to let go with both hands, the child claps his hands, at first only in front of the body as he has already learned to do when sitting. He can catch hold of a rung at once, if necessary. Later, when he stands more safely, he can take his hands away for a longer time. To do this the mother teaches him to clap his hands above his head. To learn to stand independently for a longer and longer time, mother and child count how often the child can clap without holding on to something, so the child learns to count as well. If that is not yet possible, they both say "bim, bam, bom" for each clap and repeat it.

At first the fear of falling has to be overcome, even when the child only has to clap once. To achieve this the mother stands in front of the child and spreads her arms so that they are next to her child's arms, but she supports him only if he is about to fall down.

When the child is able to stand safely with the help of the chair he can learn to take his first steps. For this he stands behind the ladder-back chair and grips the rung at shoulder-level. His mother, who sits on the chair facing him, now pulls it backwards a little and encourages him to take a step by supporting his stepping leg. The child takes a step and holds on to the chair. If he is not strong enough, his mother can take his hand and strengthen his grip. This way independent walking with a ladder-back chair begins, step by step. Later on the child will push the chair himself when walking. At first the mother can facilitate this by sitting behind him and helping him to lift his knees higher or to stop the knees from pressing together or the legs from crossing.

At first each single step has to be taught: "I put weight on my right leg"(so the heel touches the ground), "The left leg takes a step". The goal has to be formulated in words. The activity which achieves the aim is learned only by actually reaching the aim. The heel should be kept on the ground and, to achieve this, the mother makes her child look at the ceiling or clap his hands above his head. This way his heels go down to the floor.

To prevent walking on the toes the child can wear special boots that keep the ankles at a right angle, as a temporary support or for walking a longer distance. When lying, sitting or standing, however, the child should be barefoot or wear normal shoes to learn to keep his heels down.

In later stages of walking the child moves the ladder-back chair in front of him step by step.

Then his mother can take the chair away completely. Instead she walks in front of her child with her arms apart, facing him, and calls him to come to her. From here the education of the motor-disordered child is no different from that of a normal (non-disordered) child.

The ladder-back chair is a teaching instrument for standing up, sitting and walking. It can also be used to learn how to sit down. The child stands behind the chair, grips the rung at shoulder level and grasps each lower rung alternately. Thus he "climbs down" with his hands. Then he sits down on another chair which has been put behind him.

If he climbs further down to the rungs below the seat, he learns to squat. This is an intermediate stage in learning to sit on the floor, but also in learning to support himself for safe falling. The child has to learn to fall safely as this goes with walking safely. The child must learn not to fall backwards or fall like a sack but to support himself with his arms when falling or slipping.

Mother and child rehearse in games what the child has learned with the ladder-back chair. For example in the "squat-walk game" the mother walks in front of the child and holds his extended arms; the child grips her thumbs and the mother reinforces this grip by supporting his wrist with her palms and fingers from above (the child's hand is bent slightly back). "We go for a walk, we go for a walk, and squat down on this hill...". They say this together, if possible, and walk for a bit and then squat down. Later on the child just holds on to the mother with one hand. Every little child loves this game but only the mother who does this according to the Petö system knows its importance.

Walking may also be encouraged by the child's sitting on a chair and turning in a half circle to the left or to the right, by taking little steps to the side. These movements also need to be integrated into games. This way the child also learns to separate his legs again, often a difficult task for motor-disordered children and therefore very important. Sideways stepping can also be learned at the plinth when standing, in order to learn to separate the legs and to prevent their crossing. Here the child grips the slats and takes steps to the side.

Walking sideways is an intermediate stage for independent walking. To be able to achieve this the child must be already able to move his hands from one place to another, to hold on to different things on the way to some goal. As preparation for independent walking a special "walkway" can be created with two fixed parallel bars (broomsticks) between which the child can walk while gripping them.

Together plinth and ladder-back chair are very useful in various ways. For example the plinth can serve as a table, the child sits on a chair in front of it and holds on to the slats. The child learns to sit for a long time while playing and eating. At first the child holds on to a slat with one hand while the other can be used for other activities like painting or making salt dough (made from 3oz flour and 3oz salt mixed with water). Later the mother can help her child make different things out of this dough and use both his hands at the same time. This way he also learns to behave purposefully and independently.

The plinth, the chair, and the dough are multi-purpose teaching aids which the mother can use for achieving her various educational aims. These aims support the growth of independent activity in the child's personality development.

9. Play, Language, Versatility

By practising the Petö system the mother aims to change her child's personality so that he becomes "totally normal". In this process ("metamorphosis") she recognizes the features of motor-disorder as obstacles to the child's personality development and looks for ways to overcome them. In this respect it is an oversimplification to say that the mother teaches her child to sit for an ever-lengthening period of time and also to use his hands. She looks on the one hand for an occupation which encourages her child to sit for a long time, on the other hand she tries to achieve a particular educational aim with this activity. The mother of a motor-disordered child is aware that flicking through a picture book not only teaches fine movements of the fingers but also sitting for an extended period, developing the sense of balance. The child's attention is on the pictures which the mother describes. She explains what is to be seen in the pictures: people, animals, plants, objects, colours, what happens and so on. She shows what is big and small, on the right or on the left side, or at the top and at the bottom. The child is interested in everything and listens intensely. This way he not only learns to know the world but at the same time learns to use his hands and to keep his balance for a long time in a sitting position.

Connecting various and different learning processes is a vital part of play and the whole wonderful effect of the mother's educational effort shows itself at its best in her child's play. But the mother teaches her baby from the beginning to play not only with her but also on his own. As the child gets older and learns to sit at a table, she can fix a sheet of paper on the table (with adhesive tape), give him a coloured pen and encourage him to draw something. The child should choose the colour of the pen for himself and the mother tells him the name of the colour. She takes care that he grips the pencil correctly, having chosen an appropriately thick one, that his knees are correctly bent and also that his soles and heels are on the ground. She may have to hold his child's hand with her own, so that he holds the pen tightly. They draw together and sing a song. The mother has already shown him on her own face or on his, where head, hair, eyes, and mouth are and what they are called. The child has pointed at everything with extended arms, afterwards pointing at his own face as well. This way he learns eye-hand coordination. Now he sits independently and draws a doll in front of him and talks to himself: "This is the eye, this is the nose...".

Not only is the mother's educational work multi-faceted, it is also performed continuously during the whole day, as long as the child is awake. The child learns to coordinate various movements in an increasingly effective way and to overcome the problems of motor-disorder. His movements become more and more "normal".

He also learns to speak. He understands more and more, can express himself better and finds his way in the world.

The mother's education never progresses mechanically, never follows schematic rules, but satisfies the child's needs, wakens his interests, develops them further and increases his faculty for cooperation.

The child enjoys the results very much. The main reason for this is that not only is he helped by his mother but he also helps her. The mother expects this help and is happy when she gets it. This way the child learns independence, is able to find his own way and becomes more and more self-assured. This is because the mother has never tried to inhibit the child's activities but always encouraged him and channelled his energy in the right way. The mother of such a child enjoys her achievements more and more, they increase her self-confidence and strongly motivate her to go on.

When feeding her child the mother is interested not only in her child's appetite but also in the way that she can teach him to hold the spoon. At first she not only has to look after his grip but also to make sure that he sits securely. It takes a long time before a child helps to fill the spoon or put it into his mouth. This learning process makes meals last longer. How often the food is spilt! How long it takes to clean up! But learning is going on! (It is advisable to cover the area round the child.)

The mother should never use a bottle with a teat as this teaches the child nothing that can be developed further. Instead he should use a spoon and a two-handled mug, which he learns to hold independently. As soon as he is ready, he gets a piece of crust in his hand and is fed with solid food. This way he learns to chew, which is an intermediate stage for speaking.

Now the child has learned a lot of skills for solving various tasks. He takes more and more part in feeding, dressing, and washing and becomes more independent in these activities. He starts to rub soap on his chest and tummy when bathing, and to take off and later to put on trousers and socks. Not only does he learn the names of garments but also their colour and pattern, whether they are clean or dirty, and much more. The mother is not normally interested in results of psychological tests but she is glad that her child is able to eat with spoon, fork and knife - although at first they have to have thick handles - that he not only understands things, but also talks logically and has an increasing vocabulary. She reports enthusiastically if her child has said something funny.

The mother will have more and more success in finding all the opportunities to use in her educational work. She realizes that various things in her surroundings can be used for educating her child. Even a simple spoon becomes an instructional tool when she explains to her child where the handle is and how it is shaped, whether it is straight or curved, or full or empty. To experience the symmetry of the body, she makes the child hold the spoon with the left and the right hand, alternating every day.

She also teaches her child to use things in different ways. For example a rubber ball can be pressed, rolled or thrown. With the help of such a ball the child can learn to squat and keep this position when the ball is rolled between the child and another person opposite.

Even a coloured rubber ring or quoit, six to seven inches in diameter and an inch thick, is useful in many ways. It is for example a "hat" which is put on and taken off again with both hands. With this the mother aims to develop symmetrical stretching and bending of the child's arms and the performance of specific movements, directed by tactile and kinaesthetic perception.

With the ring placed between two of the slats of the plinth, the child can hold it with one hand while eating with the other.

Dr Petö was very proud of his discovery that if a child is given a ring for each hand (in the beginning they used sticks), which he has to squeeze tightly, he can do things which until then had been too hard, for example getting up from a chair without help. The "energetic" effect of squeezing was already known in diagnostical neurology but until Petö this knowledge had not been used therapeutically for learning.

Accordingly the mother gives her child a rubber ring in one hand, so that he is able to draw better with the other. She can also give him two rings and thus help him put his heels on the ground when walking. He can use the spoon better when squeezing another spoon with the other hand. The mother must, however, always remember her child's individuality. What is good for one motor-disordered child does not have to be good for another. The mother should always choose the aid and create those conditions appropriate for achieving a certain goal.

10. The prognosis of motor-disorder

Up to now we have tried to persuade the mother of a motor-disordered baby that there are ways of overcoming her child's difficulties.

Here we want to add an important warning. Only during the first three years does the mother have the wonderful ability to promote her child's personality development. After that her influence diminishes, for further development of the child's personality now requires a greater amount of personal contact, most of all with children of the same age. If it has not been possible to overcome the child's difficulties in the first three years, it takes more complex relations than that of mother and child to overcome these difficulties later.

Here we also want to talk about the role that the father and brothers and sisters play in the personality development of a child.

When a child lives in a family, naturally all members of this family influence his personality development. We concentrated on the mother because in most cases it is she who feeds the baby and takes care of him from the beginning, and therefore has an incomparably higher influence on his personality development than other members of the family. They generally have an indirect influence by supporting the mother's educational work but sometimes also by hindering it. If the members of the family play an intensive part in the daily educational work to overcome the child's difficulties, his state will improve surprisingly quickly. They can take part by doing things with him and also by helping the mother with household and other tasks.

It is true that the mother has an incomparably greater influence on the personality development of her child in the first three years than any other person but this does not mean that she can start the Petö system at any time in this period and do this successfully. If the mother does not do things with the child in the first months using the Petö system, he does not get the necessary education for his personality development. Every passing month increases the time that is necessary for overcoming difficulties, which means that the prognosis worsens with age. If the Petö system is not started until several years have passed, irreversible features are added to this late start (symptoms become worse although the original brain damage remains unchanged).

The brain functions that manifest themselves as personality develop in addition to the brain functions that exist from birth and those that develop as facets of maturation. This additional development influences functions that change substantially and form more and bigger functional entities ("patterns"), revealed in the increased performance level of the child. It is the mother's task to enlarge these functions, according to the child's needs.

A newborn child is much more independent than many people think. He has highly complicated functions controlled by the central nervous system, like breathing, blood circulation, heat-regulation, and so on.

The most complicated metabolic processes are regulated by the child's brain functions from birth; the mother only has to supply food. Later on it is enough to put food in front of the child and he will eat by himself.

Independence and the ability of a healthy child to cooperate develop relatively quickly and extensively in the first three years. However, a severely motor-disordered child stays at his initial level of achievement and falls more and more behind children of the same age without appropriate Conductive Education. In cases of very slight motor disorder an extraordinarily capable and energetic mother with a very observant eye will "instinctively" find the right way to overcome her child's difficulties. It is not easy to say which cases are to be called mild ones. The later the appropriate treatment starts, the greater the lost time that has to be recovered and the more time will be needed for overcoming or reducing symptoms. A motor-disordered baby can catch up with children of the same age with the help of the Petö system in a few months; a three-year-old child with the same damage, however, will take years to do so. In both cases the child is able to catch up on the personality development of children of the same age and then keep pace with them.

This means that the prognosis for the development of a motor-disordered child depends upon the point of time when the Petö system is started. However, this does not mean that children who start the system rather late, perhaps at an age of three or four years, can no longer overcome their difficulties. It is precisely this success with older children that has made Conductive Education famous in many countries.

The question of the mental development of motor dysfuctional children does not have to be dealt with, as this development is associated with general personality development and overcoming difficulties. The notion that motor-disordered children are always mentally handicapped is widely held but totally wrong.

It is true that motor-disordered chidren often show a delay in mental development but this is only the effect of insufficient experience and activity and of inappropriate interaction with the child. A child who is severely affected in his movements and whose lethargic behaviour is often misinterpreted as being quiet or well behaved, but who cannot activate his mother so that she plays interactively with him, will never have the experiences necessary for mental development. A child who is not able to grasp a rattle will never develop a sense of space. It is tragic to think that a mother may be glad about not being disturbed by her "good" child and does not know what to do with him - except to care for him. Thus the child remains isolated and neglected, and becomes lethargic. These lethargic, motor-disordered infants live in a inhuman world, excluded from reality.

When a mother teaches her child to hold a mug she teaches him at the same time that the thing he holds is a mug, that what he drinks is tea and that it is warm and sweet, and so on. Thus the child gains more and more tactile, visual, auditory and linguistic experience and adapts himself to human surroundings. He starts becoming a human personality, his "anthropogenesis" starts and is developed further in "anthropogenic cooperation". In this development it is impossible to draw a distinct line between activities and mental abilities. This is true both for healthy and for handicapped children whose personality development has been set in motion. It may also happen that previously motor dysfunctional infants who have been taught by the Petö System become exceptionally lively, bright and assertive, compared to infants who have been healthy from the beginning, due to their particularly intensive interaction with their mothers.

11. Theoretical Aspects of the Petö System

A chapter from the as yet unpublished book *The Meaning of Human Life* (*Relational Psychology*) by Akos and Akos.

Following the section on cerebrally damaged children and Conductive Education, we think that it is time to discuss theoretical issues. This discussion will also give us an insight into issues of general importance.

The medical literature about motor-disordered children is inadequate in its theoretical content. It can neither give a clear picture of the affected children's situation nor provide sufficiently useful therapeutic instructions. Specialists agree that the symptoms of motor-dysfunctional children are caused by brain damage. They do not agree what sort of brain damage it is and how it is connected with the symptoms. Research into the brain supplies a lot of detailed knowledge, but unfortunately this is not very useful for motor-disordered children. It is generally believed that structural brain damage is irreversible. However, often the symptoms increase with age, but sometimes they diminish or disappear totally. Various theoretical reasons are given for therapeutic methods of treatment of handicapped children but these do not agree with each other.

In such a situation it is always best to return to the starting point in order to orientate oneself; in our case we return to movements. We have to define exactly what we are talking about. To avoid losing ourselves in small, practically useless details, we will confine ourselves to natural movements. It is known from previous research that even the most simple natural movements depend upon many muscle fibres working together. This works according to a sequential pattern and is regulated by extraordinarily complicated brain functions.

This fact does not prevent a mother from doing things successfully with the natural movements of her child. This shows that simplicity in biological questions is not attainable by splitting up individual components.

To examine children's natural movements we will turn to the mother's experiences. As a starting point we will take the natural movements of a newborn baby, which are exceedingly complicated but still more simple than those of older people.

The natural movements of a newborn baby can be divided into three groups. The first group contains movements like, for example, breathing. The mother is generally not concerned with these movements. If there is something out of order she will consult a doctor. These movements are called "autonomic" and we will not discuss them further.

Of the second group of the newborn baby's natural movements, crying is the one that most attracts the mother's attention. These movements of crying stimulate the mother to do things with her baby. Sooner or later he will stop crying because of his mother's cooperation with him. It may be enough if the mother goes to her child, talks with him and strokes him. The crying will stop and a new movement become visible; the features relax and the baby becomes quiet and content. Perhaps his activity stops and he falls asleep.

Crying, as a movement of the child, has initiated the mother's movement (activity) which in its turn caused a change in the child's movements, the signs of contentment. Finally his activity stops, which ends the mother's activity for that particular episode.

Another example: The mother realizes that her child is crying because he is thirsty and gives him something to drink. As is to be expected, he stops crying and begins to drink. Here we also find a change of movement. The new movement does not take long and the child turns his head away. We can see that he is content.

The natural movements of this group are not very varied in newborn babies. Seen from the mother's perspective they are all able to promote her own activity, to support or to stop it. The mother's activities comply with the child's movements, that means the mother is always active for concrete reasons. She looks for a reason for the baby's crying, most of the time she soon finds out why, and also says so. She tells the baby that he is hungry or thirsty, cold or warm, that he has wet himself or that he was frightened. The mother's individual activities thus combine with the child's movements, and give rise to cooperative action towards a goal. We call this group of the newborn baby's movements "cooperative (indirect) expedient movements".

However, the baby's activites are not restricted to these movements. From the mother's point of view there are also "casual and non-expedient movements" as, for example, the thrashing and kicking of arms and feet.

All movements - the autonomic and the two groups of infantile activity - are an expression of complicated brain functions. The brain with its impenetrable complexity of specific functions resembles a "black box". This means that only the results of its total functioning are visible, for example as natural movements. On the basis of the coordinating and integrating general function some specific functions of the "black box" can be understood. The total functioning is not a simple combination of specific functions, but the meaning of some specific functions becomes clear if the whole is considered. We can therefore go from the whole to the parts; in our case from the group of natural movements to the three individual groups.

This differentiation between three different groups of movements allows certain conclusions about the brain function of the newborn baby to be drawn. The brain organizes three different types of movement. When we look at the changes that are caused by maturation, we find that age cannot influence autonomic activity, but that the two other groups are highly dependent upon it.

In the course of time a new group, which becomes increasingly significant emerges from the group of cooperative, expedient movements. It can be called "acquired, expedient movements". An example: At first the mother lets her baby drink from a bottle. Soon he will grab the bottle, then a mug, later on he will lift it independently and still later put it carefully on the table. Then the child will take care that he does not spill the fluid on his clothes or on the carpet...but we are racing ahead of ourselves.

Newly acquired expedient movements are constantly added to the cooperative (indirect) expedient movements, and this enables the baby increasingly to satisfy his needs on his own. This way more and more cooperative expedient movements are changed into acquired (direct) expedient movements. These movements can be called acquired because they develop out of the mother's cooperation and are a substitute for it, they imitate and copy the mother's activities. When cooperating with her child the mother is not only led by his needs but also by the values of family and society. Thus a European child learns to eat with knife and fork while a Japanese child learns to use chop-sticks.

From this change of movements the conclusion can be drawn that inherited (congenital or maturationally developed) physiological function changes step by step to a human-biological function. This makes the baby increasingly independent. The partial or total lack of this change - and thus the dependence of the child - causes the parents of a motor-disordered child much worry. We now want to look into the conditions that lead to the human-biological change in the newborn baby's brain functions.

Increasingly the mother experiences that her infant helps her, then takes over from her and so becomes more independent. This change is interpreted and encouraged by the mother as learning. For example, when feeding the child she gets the impression from the awkward and fidgety movements of his hands that he wants to hold the bottle, so she holds it in a way that enables him to succeed. Then she holds his hands, so strengthening his grip, and lets him drink. She gives the child time to help lift the bottle. This then makes his activity meaningful (after satisfying his thirst); it has proved a functional expedient activity. In the brain's functioning a progressive feedback control system develops, in which the anticipated goal is strengthened through re-afference. These efforts become increasingly efficient through use in similar situations.

The "raw material" for the mother's teaching is supplied by casual, non-functional movements. Her teaching activity may be compared to a phenomenon often observed in biology: that chance variations present the items of choice for selection. The mother can choose from the infant's casual movements those which are most appropriate to her activity, she can use them and so reinforce them in a learning process. The competing, less useful variations of movement gradually diminish.

There are several competing patterns at the level of brain function. The pattern that dominates has adapted itself best to present conditions and gained over initially similarly strong patterns, rendering movements more and more differentiated and appropriate to circumstances. Competition also takes place at higher levels of brain function.

Thus in the field of movement we have a phenomenon similar to that which the Russian scientist Pavlov discovered, concerning the distinction of sensory perceptions by conditional reflex. Firstly a being acquires the ability to distinguish gross differences before being able to make gradually finer differentiations. Sensory perceptions which are similar cannot be differentiated at first.

In similar situations the infant's brain suggests similar variations of movement, like fidgeting with the hands. From these available movements the mother chooses the one which she can use best. Thus she selects but she is not aware of choosing the most appropriate movements from a set of variants. This enables her to teach her child to become more dextrous in his various movements. The infant's brain function produces the variation which the mother uses for positive selection in the form of casual movements. The dependence of motor-disordered children, therefore, is caused by a lack of casual movements from which the mother can select those to be learned by the infant.

Contrary to healthy infants, whose casual movements of undifferentiated fidgeting and thrashing change into complex and varied movements within some weeks or months, infants with motor-disorder do not show these changes. Their casual movements are very limited from the beginning (for spastic children) or they are gross, shapeless, unfamiliar "hyperkinetic" movements (excess movements of children with athetosis), that do not diminish with increasing age, but rather increase. Without appropriate Conductive-Educational help the mother cannot use these movements in her interaction with her infant.

It is the fact that casual, non-functional movements do not change which hinders the development of learned functional movements, rather than the infant's symptoms. These children make it impossible for their mothers to educate them towards independence.

If, however, the mother learns to integrate her infant's movements into their joint activities and if she realizes when and to what extent she can reduce her support, his casual movements will gradually become more precise, varied and exact. This explains why it is no help to cerebrally damaged children if one tries to inhibit their symptoms by abstract tasks or to reshape their movements into functional ones by exercises and training.

The only correct method starts by encouraging the initial casual and non-functional movements and so promoting the basis for learning functional movements.

Before we discuss ways in which this can be done, we first have to discover why a child learns the movements that his mother has selected. To understand this we turn to the role of motivation. Every time a person starts being active, there is some motivation behind it. If for example an infant cries, he draws his mother's attention to the motivation which triggered off the action. A content face shows the mother that the motivation died away when the aim was achieved and so stopped the initial activity.

So motivation represents a particular period of activity which has a certain aim and which ends after achieving it. Achieving the aim then confirms the appropriateness of the activity. In this way the movements leading to the aim are learned. The help given by the mother is combined with the movements in the infant's period of activity in such a way that the movements of both the mother and her child form a "dialogue" that results in the infant achieving his aim. At first it is only the mother who is able to organize the infant's activity effectively by her cooperation. She makes use of the child's casual movements which become increasingly dextrous owing to this Conductive Education.

At first the child is able to drink (to return to this example) only with the mother's cooperation. Soon she finds that her child helps more from day to day and becomes more dextrous. He gets better at holding his head up, opening and closing his mouth, and so on. These partial movements are selected by the mother from various available casual movements. The child learns them as they have satisfied his needs.

This helps to explain why a child when drinking learns to grip a mug, to hold it, to lift it up, but not why he learns to put it down again. This movement takes place after achieving the goal - the above explanation does not therefore fit here.

There must be motivations other than satisfying physiological needs, which also lead to the acquisition of functional movements.

Whenever the mother begins to do things with her child she realizes that this increases his activity, in other words a new motivation has arisen. This motivation is especially important because of the infant's growing contribution to the mother's activities. So he not only learns the activities that lie immediately before achieving his goal but all the others in this period of activity too. The initial casual movements are mostly non-purposeful and do not satisfy a need. Some of them, however, are treated as helpfulness by the mother and to these she reacts with an expression of content, with a friendly voice.

It is precisely this which is the biological goal of such "secondary motivation" of the infant, through which he learns movement. The secondary motivation thus consists of securing the mother's contentment. It is triggered off by the child's wish to satisfy her. It dies away when the mother is content.

If the mother does more with her child, this motivation will appear again and again in subsequent activities. This may explain why a child learns to put down a mug.

The infant assists his mother in their collaborative satisfaction of his needs (his primary motivation); the mother reacts to this with an expression of contentment (his secondary motivation); this makes her education for independence more effective.

It can be seen that casual movements increase with the infant's motivation. Now we return to a question which arose with motor-disordered children: how can the hampered development of casual, non-functional movements be set in motion?

The answer is clear: firstly, motivation has to be intensified; secondly, even the smallest attempts at movement have to be recognized and supported educationally. We have already shown how this can be done.

What kind of motivation, however, can be intensified? Generally, motivation must not be intensified if its goal is reached by the mother's cooperation with the child in satisfying his needs. If a hungry or thirsty child is kept hungry or thirsty, this may him do harm.

It is much better to intensify the child's motivation to support his mother's help, if she learns to recognize and to promote her child's attempts at movement and to guide them so that he achieves his goal. It is precisely these attempts which the mother can and should support by words of encouragement, by demonstration and by help.

Up to now we have not considered the motivation which makes a newborn infant play. How strong this motivation is can be seen with older children who can hardly be tempted with lunch when absorbed in an interesting game. This motivation to play already exists in a newborn child. In some ways here he is already independent, though he likes the mother to join him in playing.

The goal of play-motivation is not so immediately recognizable to the mother as that of motivation to make indirect functional movements. But she does realize when the infant plays and knows that he enjoys doing so very much. The mother takes delight in the child's enjoyment when she joins him in play. The goal of play-motivation is a qualitative and quantitative development from the group of casual, non-functional movements, as well as growth in experience, and is part of orientational ability. When playing, the child's movements become more precise and differentiated. So their range increases, coordinating connections develop and movements become more dextrous. This opens up the world to the child.

This gradual change in the infant's movements makes the mother's educational work possible and is from the outset part of the development of orientation. Gradually this becomes the most essential goal of play-motivation. This can be clearly seen from the fact that only those games which attract attention and bring new experiences or confirm old ones are interesting. It also explains why motivation to play is so strong and why playing has such an important meaning for the child's personality development.

Therefore, motivation to play already exists almost continually in the newborn infant. It diminishes with tiredness but only switches off entirely during sleep.

One can see in a healthy infant that he starts practising to grip objects, letting go and picking them up again very early, so learning hand-eye-coordination.

As an infant greatly enjoys playing with his mother, the impulse for playing with a dysfunctional child has to be initiated first of all by the mother, to encourage natural change in his movements and to increase his dexterity. Secondly, she has to increase her infant's motivation to want to help her. The development of impaired casual movements can be initiated and encouraged, as it is in healthy children. This makes possible the development of the whole personality of motor-disordered children and their independence.

This may get clearer if we compare the child's brain to a computer. However, this comparison as with any other comparison, is not entirely accurate. If it is accepted, we can say that the computer of the dysfunctional child is basically all right. His brain functions differ from those of a healthy child only in the programming of the inherited (innate or maturational) casual movements.

The human brain can be compared with a computer in that it is constantly reprogrammed. For this partial programmes of casual movements are necessary, integrated by the mother's cooperation into more complex programmes. It is true that the symptoms of motor-disorder are caused by defective partial programmes; for further development, however, these are not decisive. The crux of the matter is the impaired development of the group of casual non-functional movements, and the non-appearance of these movements' growing differentiation and variation. To be able to give the necessary help the mother has to support the child's motivation both for play and for helping her (becoming independent). In her educative cooperation the mother can compensate for the defective partial programmes in the same way as she would with the initially clumsy movements of a healthy infant.

Only there is no deletion of the defective partial programme in this computer; it can not simply be replaced by an intact one. This helps to explain why an illness may be enough to revive previous symptoms even if the process of overcoming the difficulties of a motor-disordered child has already successfully started. The compensatory pattern is not yet strong enough to dominate. The same is true with a premature end or interruption to the Petö System; this may mean that movements which were not sufficiently strengthened will be lost again and the child's condition will worsen, whilst old symptoms may even occur again.

Because biologically the mother has the "monopoly" over her child's personality development during the first three years, she is trained as "programmer" in the Petö System. The advantage here is that she is expected to do what she would be able to do spontaneously under "normal conditions". The only difference is that she will need instruction in this aggravated situation. (These instructions are mainly practical ones and require the use of simple equipment.) It is not very surprising for a mother to be told to occupy herself with her child constantly during the day, since any mother would do that with her healthy child anyway. It is not difficult either for a mother to discover when she is playing with her child satisfactorily; this she can see from the child's happiness, the lessening of his symptoms and the increase in his independence. It is basically the same for older children. Only the conditions governing the "programmer" and the education change.

We think that we have made it sufficiently clear why the motivations which support the child's attention and activity are central to the Petö System. Consequently there are neither exercises without motivation, nor passive exercises, nor forced inhibitory measures, in Conductive Education. We have tried to explain why a child learns natural movements in the Petö System. Abstract movements ("exercises") cannot be developed naturally and be integrated into practical activities.

In summary we want to state that Conductive Education is not a "method" in the usual sense but practising a way of life orientated towards healthy, happy children, but under conditions which make personality development more difficult.

This is of general importance since changes in infantile movements represent the beginning of human-biological, functional alterations of the brain, of general personality development. The example of motor-disordered children shows that there is an effective route towards successful development, even under unfavourable conditions of learning and teaching.

Part II: A Mother Fights for her Child

25 January 1985

A letter from Eva Galla:

The enclosed article was published in a local magazine. Have you heard about it?

Can you remember me telling you about a friend of mine who has a motor-disordered child? She read this article as well and was interested in it. She called me and we talked about it.

Note
In Shirley Thompson's article "A child can laugh again" the case of four-year-old Jenny Wallace is described. The little girl, who is spastic, was sent by her parents from Dundee (United Kingdom) to Budapest to be treated at the "Institute for Training of Behaviour", founded by András Petö.

She said that she was able to travel to Hungary with her child as her husband works for the railways and so the family can travel cheaply in Germany.

I told her that the easiest way would be if she contacted you, as you speak German. She should write you a letter about her problems and ask you questions. I gave her your address and I think that she will contact you soon. Her child is one-and-a-half years old now...

2 February 1985

To Eva Galla:

Thank you for the article. Before now we had not heard about it and we read it with great joy.

If your friend writes to us, we will suggest that she comes here with her child, so we can have a look at her - free of charge of course.

Most probably we will explain to her what to do with her child and tell her to come back a month later. If the child is not more than one-and-a-half years old, her mother can do a lot for her. But she should not wait any longer. The infant's future depends on how well her mother understands and carries out her tasks. If she wants to take our advice we will explain everything to you as well: the child's situation, the possible results and the way to achieve them.

It may well prove very important that you are able to explain more to this mother, as you live near her.

By the way it looks like the British have started to be interested in the Petö-system. The British Minister of Health was in Budapest and visited the Institute. Students from the University of Birmingham will come in March to learn...

13 February 1985

From Caroline Seiffer:

I got your address from Frau Eva Galla who is a friend of mine. She told me about your work and that is why I am writing to you about my little daughter and asking you whether you can see a way to help her a bit more.

My daughter is twenty months old. I also have two healthy daughters, aged six and eight years. I had the youngest, Dina, at the age of 38; she was a twin. In the thirty-fifth week of pregnancy it was discovered that the other twin (who was identical) had died and a few days later a Caesarean section was done. Dina weighed five pounds, one ounce and was 19.3 inches long, nothing peculiar. She did not have to be put into an incubator and I could take her home after ten days.

I saw at once that she was different from the others as she often stiffened herself and had difficulties with drinking. At the age of four months she was still not able to fix her gaze or to smile. The physicians used to console me with the fact that she was a premature baby. At the age of five months I took her to a

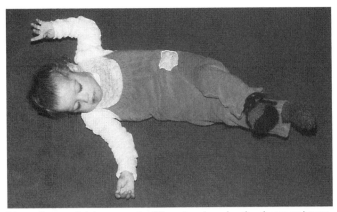

Dina at the age of eighteen months. When she relaxes her thumbs are no longer fixed in the hand but they are not yet free either. She lifts her head a little and this way she can follow her feet movements with her eyes. She makes an effort to lift her leg a little and succeeds.

centre for spastic children. The physicain diagnossed a " not very light cerebral damage". He advised me urgently to do Vojta's method of exercises. I hope that you know this method.

Here the child is made to do movements which she cannot do on her own. This is supposed to decrease the muscular tension, so she does not relapse into so-called "patterns". I have done this with Dina for 14 months and I think that there is a certain amount of success.

Additionally, she is treated with the Bobath method three times a week, which she likes very much.

Dina is now twenty months old, she cannot sit on her own, but can keep straight with a little support; she does not throw her head backwards any more and can keep it upright quite easily. She supports herself very slightly at the sides but she is not yet able to hold or keep her position. She can crawl forward by bending her legs alternately, but still has difficulties with her arms.

When lying on her front her arms are in front of her and she can lift the right or left arm alternately to get toys. She is interested in toys now, too.

Dina at the age of two years. She sits in a bad, passive way which unfortunately is common here. Besides this the legs cannot support the trunk and thus the spinal column has no support either. Sitting in a corner allows no freedom of the arms nor does it prevent scoliosis. The strong spasticity of the child can be seen in her arms and legs and suggests that she does not feel too safe. At this age Dina was able to overcome the spasticity when she felt safe. But even a year later she would go rigid, bend her arms convulsively and bend her head too far backwards ("opisthotonus") when frightened.

She can focus on things well, but squints; she recognizes people, and is scared of strangers. The physicians here have always been positive about her mental development.

There is considerable muscle tension in her legs: when she is standing they stiffen and cross.

I hope that I have given enough information for you to form an opinion about my little girl. Do you see a chance of Dina's ever being able to learn to sit, stand, and walk?

I would be very grateful if you could tell me more about your method. I could bring Dina to you if you think it could be useful. If this is the case, how often would we have to come to you and what costs would we have to meet? ...

To Caroline Seiffer:

We received your letter today and you have described Dina's situation clearly. The problem now depends on you, her mother. If you can give Dina your whole day, she will be totally healthy, like a normal child, in one or one-and-a-half years' time.

You should not do exercises with her but do things with her, that is mainly play with her, the whole day long. You should know that every child's so-called spontaneous development is a process of learning in which the mother teaches her child, but without being aware of it. It is difficult to teach children with brain damage. That is why mothers need help with their educational activity.

At Dina's age it is obvious that you are the only person to be considered as "teacher". This changes as a child becomes older but rehabilitation takes longer then.

If you can come to Budapest for one day once a month, I will dedicate one hour to you and Dina and show you what to do with her. My instructions will be free of charge.

I hope I have answered your questions. If there is anything that you still have questions about, please write to me.

8 March 1985

From Caroline Seiffer:

I thank you very much for your letter. Up to now there have been no German physicians who have given me any hope for Dina. They say only: "We do not know what will become of these children, you have to wait."

Note on "Waiting":
  The possibility of treating motor-disordered children success-fully is only lessened by waiting. The symptoms become worse

and stronger over time, so it takes them longer to overcome their difficulties.

I want to do everything that you propose and am quite ready to dedicate myself intensively to Dina.

The only difficulty is the long journey. I want to propose the following: the first time that I come to you will be without Dina for a detailed talk; I am sure this is the best as I can test out whether I can take Dina on a train journey of nearly twenty-four hours or whether we have to fly, which I could not do very often owing to the costs.

I could arrive on March 26th at 14:25 in Budapest and come to you immediately...

26 March 1985

Meeting with Caroline Seiffer:

Frau Seiffer came to see us today. The essential facts that we learned about Dina from this talk and the photos can be summarized as follows.

Dina is a child with a severe cerebral dysfunction. She has paralysis affecting all limbs ("tetraplegia" or "double hemiplegia"). We told the mother that her daughter's condition did not justify pessimism about her future. But it was high time that the Petö System was begun, to prevent further delay.

Initially we had advised the mother to see us once a month with her daughter. At the same time she could have visited the Petö Institute to be instructed practically (we do not have any equipment) and we could have added to this with further explanation.

We had to recognize, however, that the family lived too far away. This thwarted our first plan, for a monthly journey to Budapest would be impractical for Frau Seiffer.

This was a challenge to us. We knew what would happen if Dina did not get adequate treatment from her mother. How could we help her? The only way that we could see was to show the mother what to do with her child. So we explained to her why she should give up gymnastics and instead play with her child a lot. We demonstrated the "Pat-a-cake, pat-a-cake, baker's man" game and also how to teach her child to slide backwards on her back. (More about this later.)

To tell the truth we were not very happy that we had not seen Dina at least once.

And then we had to wait for more than a month before the first news about her reached us.

3 May 1985

A letter from Eva Galla:

Caroline talked enthusiastically about her visit to you. She was here today and asked me to translate her letter to you:

Letter from Caroline Seiffer:

Four weeks have passed since my visit to you. Now I want to give the promised report about Dina. We do not do exercises any more and Dina has since become more happy and relaxed, she is no longer scared of strangers and tries to speak. She has been able to turn from her back to her front for two weeks now and in the last few days she has tried to turn from her front on to her back. When lying on her back she lifts her head and stretches her arms as if wanting to sit up. She always practises these things enthusiastically.

Now I have a question: Dina does not yet sit. If I sit her up, she falls either backwards or forwards and does not support herself. What can I do to teach her to sit?

14 May 1985

To Eva Galla:

Today we received Caroline Seiffer's letter from you.

As you will have seen straightaway you will have to help us, as this "correspondence course" is no easy task. It is helpful that you get some insights into the problem through your translation. Probably these insights will be interesting for you and, by talking about her problems with you, Caroline Seiffer will understand her task more easily. You do not have to translate her letters, but it will help if you read them and talk about them with her. I myself find it very agreeable to be able to write my answers in Hungarian.

We have to cooperate well so that the mother can understand completely what is to be done. It was extremely important to know that her child has become calmer, is no longer scared about strangers and turns on to her front alone. But she did not make it clear whether the child lifts her head only when lying on her back or when lying on her front, too.

From the photos we can see quite clearly why Dina does not yet sit. One should never take the child by the hands and pull her up to make her sit, because then the child stays passive. She should grab the mother's hand - later on - when trying to sit.

But now to more essential things.

Now and for some time to come, learning to grip and holding tight will be the the central task in Dina's education. She will only learn it by playing, at the beginning of the learning process as well as when practising.

The first thing Dina will need is a rattle shaped like a dumbbell, which she can grab easily. The mother must take care that her child grabs it correctly, with the fingers lying next to each other and the thumb opposite to them - the thumb must not lie under the fingers. The wrist is bent backwards. The mother can correct this with her own middle finger if necessary. Whatever happens the thumb must not get caught in the hand.

As soon as Dina can grab the rattle she should be given another one. With a rattle in each hand she can be taught through play to bring the hands together and move them apart again; after some time Dina will play this game on her own.

When lying on her front the first thing that she should learn is to lift her head and keep it up. Mother, father and the sisters can motivate her by standing in front of her and calling to her, singing, talking and so on. If Dina is not yet able to lift her head, a folded blanket should be put under her chest. This makes it easier to lift the head up. Later on she will no longer need this help. The mother should help her to stretch her arms so that she can support herself. Here the elbows must not give way. Later she should lift the right and the left hand alternately, and drum on the surface that she is lying on with opened hands.

This makes it clear how important a Petö plinth would be for the child, not only as a bed, but also for gripping the slats. She would learn to crawl with her head lifted up, towards her mother or a doll, when on her front. By using her hands she would learn to turn herself rapidly from front to back, that is rolling to one side, and thus changing position.

Dina can also be taught gripping when being fed. If necessary the spoon can have a thick handle. When eating she should sit straight, with soles and heels on the floor. If necessary a low platform can be put under her feet. The correct position of the feet is essential for sitting securely; it is only in this way that she can sit upright. Asymmetrical sitting encourages a tendency towards scoliosis.

When Dina grasps her spoon with one hand, the other should hold a rod of about 3 centimetres diameter. The rod is secured to the table for this purpose. This also helps learning to sit up straight.

However Dina must not be forced to sit.

The most important task now is to teach her to grasp and to hold. This will widen her ability to play.

Her mother and sisters should play with her a lot, but it is essential that her mother is aware of the meaning of the playing. Its meaning is education.

An example: The child lies on her back. Her mother pushes Dina's feet towards her bottom. Then she presses the heels gently on the base with one hand, while pressing the other hand lightly on the knees. This makes the legs extend and the child slides backwards on the smooth plinth. This will be a wonderful game for Dina, and thus she learns to bend and stretch her legs and to move backwards on her own.

The mother should encourage the child whenever occupied with her, when playing, feeding, dressing and so on, by calling, talking, pointing out the present aim and explaining how it can be reached. ("Take this in your right hand." "Pick the teddy up." "Where is the doll? Come and get it." and the like) Support must always be just enough so that the aim can actually be reached.

Even if Dina does not use both hands equally, care should be taken that she does use both hands.

It is imperative that the mother occupies herself with Dina during the whole day and encourages her; not only when feeding and dressing but also when playing. Concrete educational goals should be strived for through play. For this, gripping and holding tight is most important now. Through this Dina can learn, for example, to change place or posture of her own accord, to crawl, turn, push herself on her back always towards a goal (for example to her sister who is calling her).

Is this clear? You have to help not only as a translator here, but also by discussing the tasks. In this way Caroline Seiffer will learn to put precise questions regarding the present condition of the child.

Nobody has ever tried to practise Conductive Education under such difficult conditions. We count on the mother's creativity and intelligence, and she has already made a most positive impression on us, but we also count on your help as we know you well...

Note: How should the child be observed?

Frau Seiffer's letter from 3 May clearly shows that an unmistakable change has taken place in her child. This has rightly given the mother high hopes. She achieved this change by doing things with Dina in a new way, as we advised her to. This is how the child was stimulated.

Dina's apathy vanished and after a short time those functions which were already there but suppressed by the tortures of gymnastics and apathy became apparent. These latent, probably inherited, abilities came forward because Dina no longer had to do gymnastic exercises. Instead her mother played with her a lot. The apathy shows that the forced movements of the spastic limbs are most probably painful.

On the other hand it becomes clear that Frau Seiffer does not yet see Dina realistically. This does not contradict our positive view of Frau Seiffer, which has been further reinforced by the fact that she resisted the opposition which came mainly from the specialists and which worried her quite a lot. It was too short a time for her to realize that such general terms as "sit" are not precise enough. Sitting is not the same when sitting on a chair at a table, or on the floor or totally free on a chair. The mother of a motor-disordered child has to learn to differentiate between the child's actual condition and the concrete aim for the child.

Unintentionally, we have also contributed to Frau Seiffer's uncertainty about her educational aims by trying to create a picture of the child's condition without actually knowing her. This was not enough to help the mother realize what the concrete problems are, nor for her to be able to ask for practical instructions.

This is the reason why our first advice dealt with further perspectives in such detail.

3 August 1985

Our first meeting with Dina

It is difficult to write letters, especially to a mother who is about to learn the first steps of the Pető System.

For a long time we waited for a letter from Frau Seiffer. Then she came herself and brought Dina with her, along with her eldest daughter who helped the mother on her long journey.

They stayed one day. We wrote to Eva Galla about our experience.

4 August 1985

To Eva Galla:

Yesterday Frau Seiffer and her two daughters were here. We are writing to you at once whilst everything is still fresh in our memories.

The first steps have been very successful: Dina is active, in good humour and able to fight effectively for her goals. She has a mind of her own and this is very important. This psychological condition is essential for further development.

When lying on her front she easily keeps her head up. She crawls doggedly towards her mother but does not always move her arms and legs correctly.

As a second step we want to teach the mother how to teach Dina to grip.

As we are doing a "correspondence course" for the mother, the theoretical basis for this practical activity has to be explained, to avoid misunderstanding. The main point is that Caroline realizes she will encourage the mental development of her child by teaching her to grasp, and will see her child's increasing mobility flow from this. If Dina is ever to learn how to grasp it is essential that grasping is meaningful to her. By meaningful we mean that by learning to grasp she finds it easier to achieve her goals. A possible goal could be reaching for a toy or helping mother and so on. If, for example, the mother gives Dina a toy and she can grasp it she has reached her goal. This will make Dina strive for new aims which the mother must learn to recognize. She encourages Dina to reach these aims. She may, for example, ask Dina to give the toy back and thus Dina will learn to let go. Dina can also bang with the toy and will thus learn the connections between movement of the hand and hearing. She can also follow the grasped toy with her eyes which will teach her to coordinate hand and eyes.

The mother has to realize that her child will turn to new goals when she has achieved the older ones. Thus the process of learning continually develops if the mother adapts it to the child's striving.

At the same time the mother follows her own educational goals. She wants the child to accept her aims as her own.

Certain aims which the mother works towards can be summarized: the child should be able to do everything in a way that satisfies her mother.

The mother, however, has an additional goal, that is to care for her child and make her happy.

The mother should coordinate these two general goals - but as yet this does not work.

When Dina is thirsty, her mother gives her something to drink. That is right and important: the child has reached her aim. It is a pity, however, that they use a feeding bottle. In doing so the mother misses many opportunities for teaching. It would be better to begin to give the drink from a small mug, to teach Dina that she can drink from a mug. Then the next step must be taken, for Dina to be able to grasp and hold a two-handled mug on her own. If the mother does not take her child on her lap when eating or drinking, she can teach her to eat, drink, grip and sit at the table all at the same time. She has to watch the correct position of the fingers when gripping, with fingers lying next to each other, not one over the other, and the thumb opposite the fingers. The hand is slightly bent towards the back of the hand at the wrist, which is very important for the exertion of strength. This is what the mother strives for, but it has to be in accord with the child's aims.

We said that Dina will need a special bed, a plinth. Her mother has not yet understood the necessity of this. Obviously we did not explain it thoroughly enough. This understanding, however, would mean that the mother has realized what is necessary for Dina's mental development, that she can think in terms of such connections. The plinth as an actual bed is of minor importance; with sheets it is a hard yet springy bed that prevents scoliosis. The plinth is the best thing for learning to grip. When lying on her front the child may grip the slats and pull or push herself forwards or backwards. This is not possible on the floor! She can turn around on her front and again use the slats as help. All this involves learning to grip and change position. It is also possible to bang on the plinth with toys: hand-eye-ear coordination is learned in this way.

The width and depth of the slats and the distance between them can be calculated easily by thinking of the plinth's function.

The child will learn to stand when, lying on her front, she slides backwards down from the plinth until her legs hang down and her feet rest on the floor.

In this way the height of the plinth can be calculated. If it is too high, a low, broad stool or platform is put under the child's feet. When the child grows, the legs of the plinth will have to be raised.

Later Dina can learn to take steps to the side by holding on to the slats and walking round the plinth. Thus she will learn to move her feet and legs apart, which will remain a goal of her education for a long time to come.

It is extremely important to understand that everything that the child will later need for sitting and standing is first learned in a lying position. For example, Dina is already learning to loosen her spasticity and the resulting pressing together of her legs. This should be made into her own aim, for example by fixing two hard plastic or metal discs to the inner sides of her shoes at ankle height and showing her, as a game, how to clatter with them.

Dina learns because her mother says everything aloud that has to be done or has just been done and this way is stimulated: "I move my legs apart", "I put my legs together". If this is done well, she is praised: "That's it, did you hear the discs clatter?"

Later on she will do the same when sitting, then when standing and finally it will be enough just to say: "Hold on to the plinth and take steps to the side."

For learning to stand up and step sideways it is necessary to have wall bars fastened to the wall. They consist of rungs of different colours of about two centimetres' diameter, at a distance of thirteen to fourteen centimetres.

Anything that disturbs the process of learning should be avoided, as for example feeding on the lap and, especially, drinking with a feeding bottle.

When dressing Dina, her mother should tell her to stretch her right or left hand (or leg) towards her. This differentiation is made whenever possible. Different colours and directions should always be named too.

The equipment used is simple and in time you will be able to do without it. When learning to sit, for example, you need three little robust ladder-back chairs. The plinth can serve as a table which Dina can hold onto with one hand. This makes her more secure. Stand a chair on each side of Dina with their backs towards her. The mother can sit on each of these alternately so that Dina learns to use both hands. When Dina sits on the potty, one ladder-back chair is put in front of her, so she can hold onto it when sitting down or standing up. The two other chairs stand at each side and give her security as long as she needs it. Generally one can say that an aid is good when it can be taken away in the course of time.

Dina should playfully learn how to touch her ears and nose and how she can help her mother. What she is doing and which arm or leg (or both arms or legs) she is supposed to use must always be expressed in words so that it can be done more easily.

Her whole life is fixed into a daily routine which should be maintained so that the things which are learnt become habitual.

The mother says with every bite: "I open my mouth", "I close my mouth", "I chew", "I swallow". Dina will soon learn to swallow her saliva: "I close my mouth and swallow". Once she does it on her own it must not be said anymore.

Dina needs a lot of games, songs and rhythmic rhymes. These are always connected with the same movements so that each one is learnt as belonging to a different game.

It is essential that the mother succeeds in bringing her own educational aims into accord with those of her child. This will enable her to teach the child that what she wants her to learn.

Now the main task is to learn to grip with both hands.

I hope that this letter, which we ask you to translate and discuss with Caroline, makes it clear that she will actually deal with Dina's mental development by dealing with her movements. The activities are the results of mental development and at the same time support further developments through new experiences.

If you have any questions, please write to us. We will be glad to be able to help you and count on your help for Dina's education. "Inductive psychogenesis" is not very easy in a correspondence course but we have now seen Dina and we are optimistic.

One last thing: It is very important that Caroline should explain to Dina in a narrative way (like the narrator between two scenes at a theatre play) which goal she is aiming at, what means she is employing and what results are achieved. This will make it explicit for Dina!

15 August 1985

From Eva Galla:

Your letter of 4 August arrived in record time.

...Yesterday Caroline was here. I translated the letter in writing. She read it and said that for the first time the whole system had become clear to her. Now she knows why she should not do exercises with Dina. Exercises are exactly the opposite of what should be done because what the child wants remains unconsidered: the child is totally passive and exercises are done to her. (These are all her statements after having read the letter.)

The plinth will soon be ready.

Caroline asks: Is it better to put the child on her front or on her back when sleeping?

She also wants to know whether she may take Dina to the swimming baths. She took her once and the water was a pleasant temperature and Dina had a lot of fun. But a physician here said that swimming was not good for Dina.

Caroline has another question which, although it is no longer pertinent to herself and Dina, interests her from the point of view of underlying principles. When Dina was four months old it was recognized that she had a motor disturbance. Exercises were then started immediately as it was thought the earlier the better. She cannot, however, imagine what to do with a four-month-old child according to the Petö method. She now realizes the heart of the method but thinks it cannot be applied without a certain maturity in the child. Her question then is what you would have said if she had come to you with Dina at the age of four months. What could she have done then?

30 August 1985

To Eva Galla:

We were very happy about your letter dated 15 August that arrived yesterday.

For us it is most important now that Caroline realizes her central role as mother in overcoming her daughter's difficulties. This is part of Dina's personality development which starts with her being active and is based upon this. The mother has to comprehend this thoroughly and that Caroline now knows it is shown in her statement: "Exercises are done to her" (see your letter).

Now to answering her questions.

How is Dina supposed to lie at night, on her back or front? It does not matter. Dina herself will decide this. Which position does she prefer? She must never be forced to do anything against her will. During the daytime she prefers lying on her front, as we have seen, because she can play better there. Therefore Caroline should lay Dina on her back (!) so that she can strive actively to turn over onto her front. Her mother should guide these efforts, so that at one time she turns to the right side and another time to the left. Guidance here means that if, for example, Caroline wants Dina to turn to the right onto her front, she tells and shows her how to lift her right arm beside her head. At first Caroline shows her how to do this by taking Dina's right hand and bringing it into the desired position. She says: "I raise my right hand above my head". The lifting of the arm stops it from being pressed under the body. Now Dina needs to swing her left arm to the right side, turn head and body to the right side and finally swing the left leg over the right one. As many parts of the movements are shown and explained as Dina can understand. After some time it will suffice for the mother to say: "I turn to the right side onto my tummy."

This whole movement will develop under Dina's own power (her activity and motivation) if she wants to achieve an aim through it, for example, to look at something interesting or to get a toy. It is the mother's task to discover this aim together with the child, using anything that the child is interested in. Then she encourages Dina's striving for this aim by teaching her how to overcome the obstacles preventing her from achieving it. She must never do something on behalf of her child but must find out what her child can do on her own. In this way the child's actions will become effective. If the mother repeats aloud how the child reached her aim, she will be able to re- member the actions. Her movements combine with language and the desired aim, and this will raise the child's level of achievement.

It is right to go to the swimming baths with Dina but only if there is no danger of infection. Generally everything that Dina likes and that stimulates her is good for her. In the water her mother should play with her so she can practise what she has al- ready learnt, for example grasping correctly, kicking her legs, opening them and closing them again. If Dina holds onto some- thing she should stretch out her arms.

It would have been very advantageous if Caroline had been able to do things earlier with her four-month-old daughter using the Petö System. Basically she would have played with her in a similar way to now. Even at that age Dina would have been able to understand from her mother's talking and activity what was wanted from her. A child combines her understanding of what the mother says with what her mother does and how she behaves, and this begins during the first few months in life.

For example they could have played the following game together.

The infant grips both its mother's forefingers while the mother supports the grip with her middle fingers. At the same time she says a rhythmical rhyme, for example: "Pat-a-cake, pat-a-cake, baker's man" or something similar and moves the little fists together, and apart again. After repeating this several times she stretches the child's arms wide apart and says: "Such a big cake we bake."

Of course the child would not have been able to understand the text, but the rhythm, the melody and the sounds - with which she will soon become familiar - would have combined quickly into one unit in this active play.

With Dina lying on her back, Caroline could have played the following game with her.

She pushes Dina's feet with the soles flat on the base (plinth, table) towards her bottom and holds them there. Then she talks with her and sings a little song, for example "Cobbler, cobbler, mend my shoe. Get it done by half-past two". She accompanies this by softly beating the rhythm with Dina's heels on the base. Then she gently presses on the child's knees, so the legs are stretched. And because the feet are held Dina moves backwards and thus learns to change position.

This game can now be played with her when sitting. Dina supports herself with one hand while she knocks with the flat of her hand on the table, always in rhythm with the little rhyme.

These examples are only to show the mother that the aim with an infant is the same as now: the consolidation of achievements and support of the child's relative independence through activity under different conditions and with as many changes of position as possible.

The mother will recognize her child's increasing independence and that she now helps herself more than before, for example in bathing, dressing and similar activities.

It is most important to understand that from the beginning a newborn (!) child enters into a "mutually instructive relationship" with her mother, and can guide her in her educational work. Every mother influences her child, leads her to certain goals without being aware of it in detail and thus teaches the child. The child herself, through her needs, also guides the mother. A child with cerebral palsy, however, is not able to guide her mother and thus does not get enough help herself, not enough of the "guidance" (education) that is essential for her development.

The earlier that the mother realizes that her child's personality development is disordered, the faster she will learn from the appropriate instruction how this disorder - and thus also the symptoms of the brain damage - can be overcome at the same time as the personality itself begins to develop.

Of course Caroline can be reassured that she is not too late for her to succeed. Only what she could have achieved in one year at the age of four months, she will now reach in two or three years' work. That means that Dina will reach the developmental level of children of her own age and overcome her symptoms too.

The practical side of this method was developed by Petö, but the theoretical understanding was developed by us. Human personality develops through mutually instructive relationships; there is an "intercerebral field" between mother and child. So on the one hand the child develops more independence; on the other hand the mother teaches the child how to "stop" the symptoms of the brain damage, how to learn to grip and walk and so on.

It seems that in healthy children this process of personality development begins spontaneously, but this is not really the case. It is set in motion through cooperation with the mother, that means it is not confined to the child.

At the moment we are working on a book about relational psychology, which deals with problems of personality development, under the title: *The Meaning of Human Life (Relational Psychology)*.

We showed Caroline some photographs of Tibi from this book, a severely motor damaged child. He was four months old when his Pető treatment began. One picture shows him at the age of three-and-a-half years, running around wildly. (See pictures page 118)

By the way, Caroline is understanding the connections very quickly and well.

4 September 1985

From Caroline Seiffer:

...We had a lovely walk along the Danube in the evening, quite a treat for my daughter Elsie. After that we had two nice weeks at Lake Constance. Unfortunately Elsie caught pneumomia when we got back, she still has to be very careful.

Then my father died so I have not had any respite up to now.

Dina's plinth is ready and she sleeps very well on it; playing, turning and pulling along is not going so well but I can only start this properly next week...

9 September 1985

From Eva Galla:

Your letter arrived. I will translate it and give it to Caroline.

At the moment everything has come to a halt because Caroline has trouble in her family. After a severe illness that lasted several weeks, her father died a week ago. He lived 400 kilometres away and Caroline had to go there several times. Now she has gone to the funeral. The children are with their father...

20 September 1985

To Eva Galla:

Your letter arrived today...Caroline had already told us about her father's death...

Do you really understand our letters which you have to translate? We count on you being able to explain when necessary.

16 November 1985

To Eva Galla:

I write only because I am upset as we have not had any news about Dina for months. You have to explain to Caroline that our correspondence course is only possible if we get at least one detailed report once a month, together with photos. We have to know when Caroline is happy and when she is not. This is the only way in which we can get a picture of Dina's development and give further advice.

With these children there is a danger of a gap between physical and personality development, a gap which may widen rapidly and become very difficult to close again. We must not be careless. We are glad to be able to help but this will work only with regular and precise information...

21 November 1985

From Caroline Seiffer:

...I worked with Dina following your instructions but I must admit that there is no rhythm in it yet. She now has the plinth and the ladder-back chairs. Sleeping on this plinth is the only thing that Dina can do without difficulty, in the daytime the lying programme and pulling along the plinth are not so successful yet. I think that the reason for this is that she was already able to pull herself forwards on the floor using her arms before she had the plinth. She hardly ever grips the slats to pull herself. Instead, she likes to knock with wooden toys on the bed and enjoys the sound. Then my older daughters lie under the bed and play with her, which they all like very much. Dina lets things fall through the slots.

Note on mistaken views:

In specialist literature about motor-disordered persons one can often read that a therapy should start with gross movements and then go on to the finer ones. Dina shows the opposite of this theory (which has also been stated by Aleksandr Romanovich Luriya, the Soviet psychologist), as she is not yet able to make gross movements with her arms (e.g. pulling herself forwards with her hands) but can grip small things, put them in a slot and then let them fall.

We often practise sitting on a chair. Dina often reaches out to the right and the left looking for support. Unfortunately, she tires very quickly doing this. At present gripping presents the most problems, she keeps her thumb in too much on both sides. When she gets something to hold onto she makes scratching noises with it on the floor or on the plinth. She seems to be at a loss, not knowing what to do with things, toys for example. When lying on her back she often passes things from one hand to the other.

Notes on educationally appropriate observation

Caroline writes that her child seems to be at a loss to know what to do with things but subsequently reports the exact opposite to this. This does not mean that she is not a good observer but that she is not aware of the meaning of the things which she has observed.

Observing is a practical activity. Dina has begun playing on her own. This is an important step in her development. At pres-

ent she only does this when lying on her back. Her activity should be reinforced in this position, which seems to be especially advantageous to her, and what has been achieved in this position can then be transferred to another.

The problem then is not that the mother overlooked something but that she did not recognize the educational relevance of this observation and did not use it practically. She has not realized that her child plays with toys at a very low level of achievement, that of an infant, different from children of her own age.

Eating with a spoon is much better now; she lets me guide her hand sometimes, while she still rejects the cup violently. She grabs the cup with both hands but as soon as she realizes that it is to be taken to the mouth, she goes rigid and slides from her seat. Now I do not know whether I should force her or whether this is wrong.

She can roll over alone really well, to both sides, from her back as well as from her front, so now she can move everywhere quite fast and unerringly. She has made very good progress in this during the last few weeks.

I think it is really quite difficult to guide Dina correctly. But I am putting all my hopes on your therapy. So I am thinking of staying in the Institute for a few days if this is possible. It all looks quite different in reality. I would so much like to do everything right and sometimes I doubt whether I can do it alone.

As my mother is now able to look after my two eldest daughters I could find the time to do so. But I am not sure whether you think this a good idea. In October I had to go to the centre for spastic children, on instructions from the health insurance scheme. I already knew the doctor and he had never given me any hopes. I told him frankly that I had shown Dina to you, that I work according to your instructions and have stopped Vojta. He got very angry and said that I had to put up with the consequences on my own.

We cannot understand what this physician wanted to express by taking this attitude, because he has deprived the mother of all hope.

He was astonishingly well informed about the Petö Institute and even knows your book. He just said that it was impossible to use your method in Germany but did not say why. I will start taking pictures of Dina and send them to you. I hope that you are not disappointed that Dina has not made more progress.

4 December 1985

To Eva Galla:

I received Caroline's letter of 21 November and this letter to you is the answer to that. I begin at the end. She rightly suggested she would like to go to the Petö Institute to gain some practical experience there. This would be very good. Yesterday I talked about it on the phone with Dr Hári, the Director of the Institute. She said that there are other people from West Germany there as well and so we agreed to the following.

She can come whenever she wants after 15 January. She only has to come to the Out-Patients'Department on Tuesdays or Fridays, between 11 a.m. and 4 p.m. She will need no written confirmation. Dr Hári thinks that they should stay for three weeks. During the first week they should stay somewhere in town and come to the Institute daily. They will pay 200 forints per day, Dina will also get lunch. Caroline can eat very cheaply too. During the second and third week they can live in the Institute and thus save the cost of the flat.

Now I come back to Caroline's questions. In general we are satisfied with Dina's development. She has become more active and is now able to change her position more easily on her own and move purposefully.

But Dina must no longer drink from a bottle. To begin with Caroline can let her drink from a small cup, without Dina gripping it. This way she will learn that one can drink from a cup.

Then she should give her a mug with two handles. When she goes to the Institute she should be able to drink without a bottle.

It would also be good if sometimes the mother puts Dina on the potty. (She can grip a chair, put in front of her.)

Most probably gripping is a problem because the wrist needs to be supported from above, that is the only way for Dina to grip strongly. The best exercise might be to learn to slide down from the plinth when lying on her front, by gripping the slats with her hands and pushing herself away. At the end of this activity her feet are flat on the floor - the soles and the heels! If the plinth is too high something should be put under Dina's feet. Like this she can stand and hold herself up at the plinth. From this position she can pull herself back up onto the plinth again.

Do they practise opening the knees when lying and sitting?

When they come to Budapest we will help them to look for a flat and to get to the Institute.

Note: Cooperation with the Institute

From the beginning we intended that Frau Seiffer and Dina should visit the Institute from time to time. We do not have any of the equipment at home which is needed for showing some of the tasks. The mother can understand practical instructions better when watching other mothers and children doing the same. Different children get different kinds of help for solving the same problem, according to their individual condition. Dina will see the other children and try to imitate them.

We are very glad that they will be coming to Budapest for two or three weeks and will work in the Institute. This will speed up Dina's development and we are optimistic about this.

From Caroline Seiffer:

...My mother was here in October and so has now seen Dina again. She expressed exactly what I sometimes thought I saw, that Dina has become much less tense. When crawling she often moves her legs alternately and with the correct movement of the arms. Before she just dragged her legs along. She plays with her own hands a lot and when lying she holds her feet with her hands and plays with them. Before I had to put her in the right position for this. Her posture when sitting at meals has improved a lot. She really strives for a good posture when eating. Drinking from a mug however, is still a real problem. I have tried everything but as soon as a cup or mug or something similar comes near her mouth she goes rigid. But I am sticking at it...

9 January 1986

To Eva Galla:

...Regarding their arrival in March I have talked about everything with Dr Hári again. Everything is OK, as I said before.

It was important that her grandmother was able to see a change in Dina after only one-and-a-half months. If there is success under such difficult conditions, her development would be much faster under more favourable ones.

Today we write only about eating and drinking. Dina will never learn to drink from a mug as long as there is still a bottle in the house. Caroline should not force Dina to drink but offer her something every thirty minutes from a small cup. If she really is thirsty she will drink from the cup. This means a lot of trouble for two or three days. As soon as Dina drinks from the cup Caroline can start giving her the two-handled mug. Dina should then grasp both handles herself.

Perhaps at first she should drink in a half-sitting, half-lying position on her mother's lap, with Caroline letting the drink run into her mouth. Thus she will understand that she can drink in this way as well.

When supporting the wrist remember that the hand should be bent slightly upwards, towards the back of the hand. The position of the thumbs has to be watched as well.

4 February 1986

From Caroline Seiffer:

...I will arrive on 3 March. That is a Sunday. I would like to visit you on the Monday and then on the Tuesday I could go to the Institute. I will fly back on Wednesday, 26 March. I have to book these dates so that I can save a lot of money.

In the meantime I am taking Dina to the warm-water baths (97F). She likes it very much...

From 9 to 26 March 1986 Dina and her mother were in Budapest. At that time there was an epidemic of influenza there, so they could not be accommodated at the Institute. However it was possible to work in outpatient groups. They were in the Institute five days a week, two hours each day.

1 May 1986

From Caroline Seiffer:

Now we have been at home for a few weeks I want to report to you.

Each day we practise the programme that we learnt in the Institute and also walk several times a day. Dina did not like doing the exercises in the Institute but she likes doing them here very much. She is very good at the wall bars, pulling herself up slowly with her hands, going up on to her knees and then standing at the wall. It is still a big problem for her to stretch her arms so that she can crawl. She draws up her legs quite easily and is able to bring her bottom up, but her arms are not so good yet. We keep on practising this. We all enjoy her walking but she enjoys it most. She is very proud and today she put her left leg forward all by herself. She can sit very well on her little chair which has handles. Her gripping especially has become better and more purposeful. She can sit alone while only holding the handles of the chair. On the whole I can say that she is making good progress at the moment. She has never been so active before. A friend of mine who has not seen her for a long time also said this to me today.

Before I contacted you Dina was treated by a physiotherapist who kept on asking about Dina even after I had stopped exercises and who has given me good advice again and again. Now I have shown her all the exercises with Dina and she is enthusiastic, and she helps me with the exercises twice a week, which is a very great help for me. This physiotherapist thinks that Dina's progress is so wonderful that now she is thinking about coming to Budapest with us in autumn to see everything and to learn, so that more children in Germany may profit from this. So I want to ask you whether you think this is a good idea and whether it would be possible.

When flying from Budapest to Munich there was a woman next to us. We talked a little and she told me that she was born in Hungary and is now married to a German. She has a sister in Budapest, who was treated in the Petö Institute twenty-five years ago and who learnt to walk at the age of five. She said that she is now practically normal. Of course I liked hearing that very much.

At the moment I can manage just about everything. The only question I have is how Dina's arms could be stabilized better, so that she can lift her chest up. We use a bolster. I draw her shoulders up when kneeling behind her. This works for a short time but only with closed fists and not for very long. I have already thought about a brace for the lower arms, similar to those of the legs, so that she is forced to keep her arms straight. What do you think about that?

Dina now enjoys drinking from a cup. She no longer sucks, as she did in the beginning, but takes little sips one after the other. She reacts to questions better now as well, for example "Where is the door?", she turns her head towards it. When asking directly about people, for example "Are you fond of Elsie?" she says "No" and laughs. But when I ask her "Are you fond of the lamp?" she gives no answer and waits for the next question. She talks a lot but nothing comprehensible yet...

8 May 1986

To Eva Galla:

Yesterday we received Caroline's report about Dina. Now we are sending you the answer which we would like you to translate.

You initiated this process and we hope you are still willing to continue with it. We are all glad about Dina's successful development.

Caroline's letter clearly shows that her child's personality development has accelerated, which is relevant to her prognosis. It can be taken for granted that her further development, not only of movements but also of her mental faculties, will advance quickly. So the most important problem is solved. Caroline has learned what to do with the child. However this does not mean that she can always see the essence of the matter. This has no theoretical significance, but a practical one. Here we want to point out a danger so that she is not diverted onto the wrong path which might lead to problems. We think that we can find signs of this in some parts of her letter, where we could not understand, for example, the question about stretching the arms. We want to talk about this in further detail.

Caroline wrote that she can see progress in many fields. Dina has learned to drink, to crawl on her front, to stand up by holding on to the wall bars and to take her first steps. Caroline also wrote that Dina has become very active and cooperative, and is proud of her achievements. So it follows - and we have to see it this way - that Dina strives to reach her mother's goals. She learns that her mother is happy as a result of her own activity because she fulfils her demands and does this out of her own strength and dexterity. But it is also part of the mother's role to increase Dina's success and to learn that not everything goes the way that she wants it to.

The central question of education is to find gradually those solutions which enable Dina to reach the mother's goal. However the goal should never be an abstract one. If the mother wants Dina to stretch her arms up for a period of time, she should integrate this activity in a game. One example: Dina learns to reach this aim when sitting, holding on to the wall bars, and then tries to stand up by gripping the next higher bar. This makes stretching the arms necessary. She can learn it as well by wanting to hold a doll or another toy that lies in front of her on the plinth and creeping to it.

To learn to walk Dina needs to push a chair in front of her with stretched arms whilst taking little steps. She may have a brace (a splint) to keep the elbows stretched, but only in this situation and then only temporarily. As soon as she is able to keep her arms stretched she must not wear it anymore. (For pushing the chair forward, "sliding rails" are fastened under the chair legs so that it slides more easily and cannot fall over. Some pictures in the book *Conductive Education* by Hári and Akos show this.)

It is very important to understand - but maybe we did not quite understand the letter - why Dina does not stretch her arms. This is not absolutely necessary for crawling on her front. It becomes necessary if, for example, a red bow is fastened around a slat and a white one around another slat, about eight inches apart. Both bows are far enough from Dina that she has to grab them with stretched arms. The mother talks to her: "I grasp the red bow with my right hand." "I grasp the white bow with my left hand." "I pull myself forward with both hands." If this does not work at first the mother may push her a little bit on her bottom or thighs. The bows are moved away as she moves forward.

What Dina has learnt when in a lying position she can also practise when sitting, for example pulling off her socks on her own. Obviously the mother has to help her at first, for example by supporting Dina's grip by putting her own hand on hers. Dina's mother should gradually reduce her help and tell her child what she has achieved. This will make it clear to Dina.

We hope that we have made it clear that stretching the arms is not an isolated abstract task without any practical context, and that the mother is not helping her child by drawing her shoulders back. The difference between right and wrong help is that correct help contributes to the creation of real, natural movements which will lead to reaching the aim. Correct help can gradually be reduced and finally becomes superfluous.

The exercises that Caroline does with Dina will not always stay the same. They serve only the purpose of teaching Dina to help her mother when washing, dressing, eating, and so on in different positions. And through these activites her mother can tell her and teach her how to become more dextrous and more able to play various games with her parents and sisters. (What Caroline saw in the Institute were group activities in the form of games, in which rhythmical songs and verses created a sense of community.)

We want to stress once more here that all of Dina's aims and successes must be expressed verbally. "Here is your sock. Take it. Stretch the right hand...Now grip it strongly...Grip with your left hand too...Now we put it on..." and so on.

The objects which have been used are also named by the mother, also their colour and what they can be used for. The child will only learn to understand language if she has experiences with objects and learns their names at the same time. Of course it is confusing for Dina to be asked whether she is fond of the lamp. Caroline should ask her questions like "Where is your right (left) hand, your eyes, your mouth?" and so on. Then Dina will show the parts of the body that her mother has asked for, while her mother can support her hand. Indication of direction when lifting something up or putting it down should always be given; indication of size is important, whether something is big or small, also whether it is thick or thin, red or blue. When Dina stretches her arms or legs the mother should describe the activity with appropriate words.

This way of teaching is more important for learning to stretch the arms than are provoked movements without real, natural aims. If the child wants to stretch her arm but cannot yet do it, the mother can softly press her finger against the elbow. This is a natural form of help, in contrast to pulling back the shoulders - that is not natural.

This leads us on to the question about what a physiotherapist might see in the Institute if she goes there with Caroline in autumn. She can only understand what she sees if she takes her attention away from muscles and joints to the child's personality and is able to look at the cooperation between mother and child or between children in a group. Her training, however, hinders this approach and makes it difficult for her to adopt this point of view. If she regards what she sees there as a special form of physiotherapy, she will not have understood it. We believe that she has the best intentions but does not influence Caroline positively. The forced movements of physiotherapy are unnatural and inappropriate and hinder the learning of activities, which are aimed at reaching practical goals, and the appropriate education.

This does not mean, however, that we underestimate the physiotherapist's interest. We will be glad to help her understand the Petö System. Her question as to whether she may visit the Institute would be better asked of the Director...

We have signed a contract for the translation of the English edition of the book *Conductive Education* with a British publisher.

18 May 1986

A telephone call from Eva Galla:

"Dina started walking!"

To Eva Galla:

We were very glad about your call yesterday that Dina has started walking.

We hasten to write to you as there are new tasks to be faced now. We have to give general explanations, as we cannot watch her walking. This way we want to prevent possible problems. The following problems may occur:

1.Dina will not lift her knees high enough.

2.Her legs will be pressed together and may cross each other.

3.Her knees may not be entirely stretched when walking.

4.Her heels will not touch the ground.

We want to demonstrate how these problems can be solved.

It is very important for Caroline to think of Dina's learning to walk as an educational task. A child walks because she wants to reach a goal (motivation). There is no learning at all without motivation. A child's development only appears to go on of its own accord, but in reality the child only develops through learning, which can be achieved through education.

For example, one form of motivation is when the mother stands in front of the child and calls her with outstretched arms. The arms will keep the child from falling. Later, to increase the achievement, the mother can walk backwards.

Another goal can be that Dina wants to walk somewhere on her own. Pushing a ladder-back chair in front of her can be a temporary aid, as she can support herself with it and can stand after every step. She must not lean on it continually, that is, use it like a crutch.

A person can sit in the chair the wrong way round, preventing the chair from falling over whilst at the same time helping to push it by sliding back with it and asking Dina to follow step by step. Meanwhile walking may be corrected by showing (or simply telling) Dina how to lift her knees higher or to take care that her legs are not pressed together. At first the mother can help with her own hands.

Caroline may also help Dina by standing in front of her and preventing her legs from crossing by putting her own foot between Dina's feet. Dina strives for a certain aim, that is reaching the mother. She sees her mother and feels safe. This also diminishes the danger of falling backwards as she moves her centre of gravity forward by lifting her arms. This way her mother also has the best opportunity to observe and will know what will help Dina most at any particular moment. She must never help more than necessary, and also she should also say aloud what she is doing. For example, "I take a step forward with my right leg, put my weight on it and put my left leg next to it..." or "I take a step to the side with my right leg and put my left leg next to it." Here we aim at walking around the plinth or along the wall-bars. By learning to make steps to the side Dina will also learn to open her legs.

When Caroline teaches Dina to keep her heels on the floor, it may be useful if she lifts her head ("I look up"), or claps her hands over her head.

It is part of the process of learning to walk to be able to let oneself fall forward, but of course only onto a soft surface. This skilfull falling can be taught when Caroline pulls Dina's hands down in front of her and lets her sit down quickly in a game ("bang"). Then she can teach her step by step to stand up again: "I kneel on my right leg, I kneel on my left leg, I stand on all fours and get up." Before learning that, however, Dina should hold on to the wall bars when standing up. Each step is then anticipated verbally.

It is most important for Caroline to find out what aims motivate Dina to walk, for example coming to her mother, imitating one of her sisters, walking over to a bird's cage, and so on. The mother must always be aware of her educational aims. For example, Dina should become more independent, walk for a longer time on different surfaces, with and without shoes, squat every now and then... When squatting down she should open her knees. She should learn to climb onto pieces of furniture. However, care must be taken that she does not fall backwards.

All these activities are combined with songs, rhymes and verses; for example "Step, step, one, two, one, two. Bend down to polish my blue shoe."

3 June 1986

From Caroline Seiffer:

You will already have received the wonderful news from Eva that Dina started walking quite suddenly.

We have been practising at the chair daily and I always have to lead her legs. This works very well and Dina likes it. On 17 May I just put her on her feet in the playground because she had become so very heavy and then she just started moving her legs forward, This was fantastic for me, it was the one thing that I always wished for.

Note on sudden changes:

The report about such an important sudden change is so wonderful that the reader may be able to take a little theroretical explanation.

Our brain combines the functions of many organs and muscles in one general pattern. This pattern consists of a lot of subpatterns. All patterns occur in different variants and compete with each other. But there is always one that dominates.

Dina's former "walking" was the expression of a pattern with which her mother rightfully was not content. This dominating general pattern made the mother dissatisfied but also motivated her to create a better general pattern. The mother's cooperative efforts were a game for Dina. The new pattern was built up gradually, it got stronger and stronger until at this wonderful moment it got the better of the formerly dominant pattern.

The competition between patterns always brings about sudden changes as a new one takes the place of the old one. The necessary preparations take a long time. The mother succeeded with her patient, consistent education which recognized and used all opportunities. "Wonderful" and sudden changes are prepared for by careful, persevering work.

But why did this change become obvious exactly when and where it did?

Dina's motivation was very high because of the nearby playground as the attractions offered there were nearly attainable for her. "Wonderful" and sudden changes will never happen under boring and monotonous conditions!

In the meantime she likes walking more and is getting better at it. She wants to go to the playground all the time.

I thank you very much for your letters. In your second letter you write about the difficulties that may occur when walking. Two of them do indeed happen. She sometimes touches the ground with the toes of her left foot first and her legs often cross when walking but only at the beginning and at the end when she starts getting tired. Besides that all is going very well most of the time.

Notes on the dynamics of an activity

What marvellous observations! An old saying tells us that "the first step is always the most difficult". Everybody has to have this experience.

One can observe that the same difficulties occur when Dina is tired as when she did something for the first few times. This can be explained as follows: When a pattern dominates this happens not only because of the accumulated amount of energy, but also because of the release of energy that had been bound to the "antipattern" until then. This antipattern has had a hindering influence in the background of the pattern but now very quickly loses it. The pair of opposites, pattern-antipattern, determines the fine regulation, litheness and dynamics of an activity.

Getting tired means that the relative energy of the dominating pattern is outweighed by the increasing energy of the antipattern. Tiredness then changes the relation of strength between the two opponents in favour of the non-dominant pattern. This effects a change in the activity; walking for example becomes standing.

The spasm of motor-disturbed children is so strong because there is no antipattern that can serve as the regulator to the dominating pattern. It is because of this that existing pathological movements cannot be altered. Antipatterns to movements can and should be created in education. In this way the immense amount of energy in the dominant pattern is reduced and the relation between the rival movements finely regulated. This makes a change of dominance possible.

Normal movements and functions are always dynamically changeable and may become fatigued. It is only spasms and contractions that are tireless, continuous and convulsive.

Of course she only walks when holding my hands quite tightly. Eva said she had told you incorrectly that Dina could walk alone or just holding one hand. This is not yet possible. We still practise daily with the ladder-back chair but now in such a way that Dina walks alone, I only push an arm between her legs so that they do not cross, and that works quite well.

In my last letter I described the problem of stretching the arms. I think that my letter was a bit confusing. For me crawling means that Dina walks on her knees and with stretched arms - which she cannot do. She cannot stretch her arms in this position. Eva thinks this could be a linguistic problem; you call this "crawling" "to go on all fours". Generally Dina is now more able to stretch her arms if she wants to have something. But she cannot support herself.

In the Institute I had to sit in front of Dina and hold her arms in a stretched position, which was very exhausting for both of us and - I think - had no effect on Dina.

That is clear: There was no motivation and no activity. Dina cannot learn in this way.

Dina is now able to sit better, for about fifteen seconds, then she falls to one side, not backwards.

The letter did not make clear how or on what Dina is sitting. Caroline wrote on 1 May that she sits well on a little chair and holds herself on it without any help.

But I think that this crawling or walking on all fours is important for learning to walk independently.

With regard to walking I also want to say that Dina lifts her legs very well and does not slide or drag them. She can also step up kerbs and even tries to climb stairs but always with the support of my hand. In the street I usually walk sideways behind her and hold her arms; sometimes it even works when I go in front of her but then she is still very insecure and wobbly at the trunk.

I follow all your advice from your letters. I talk constantly with Dina, we sing and play.

At the end of the month Eva will come to Budapest, and she will bring you pictures of Dina. She has just seen her and will report to you then.

At present I have only a few questions. Should we go on using the special shoes for our training at the chair or should we use normal shoes? There are expensive special shoes for learning to walk here with additional support at the heels. A normal child does not need these shoes.

I think that I can handle everything else quite well. I want to come to you in the middle of September. I have caught your optimism and strongly believe that Dina will become healthy.

12 June 1986

To Eva Galla:

. This will be just a short letter as we will meet again soon. Today we received a letter from Caroline, now we want to answer her questions.

We think that Dina is developing very well. The most important thing in this letter is that Dina started walking on her own, that the mother realized this and encouraged her accordingly. This is a hint for the child's further development and an increase in the conductive educational ability of her mother. It is very important to watch whether the child takes initiatives which should then be encouraged. It is lucky that Caroline is such a good observer. Close observation of the child will help the mother develop the most effective means of support.

With regard to the shoes, we have to tell you that we do not know these special shoes she mentioned. Most probably Dina will not need them. At home when doing the exercises she should wear the boots with the wooden sole which she got from the Institute. They will make it easier for her to learn to put her heels on the floor and will prevent the legs from turning inwards, and so stop the crossing.

When training in a sitting or lying position Dina will be best barefoot or perhaps just in socks when it is rather cold. In this way she can aquire more quickly a feeling for the position of her feet and legs, for example whether the heel is on the floor or not. She should always be reminded and Caroline must be careful that the heels touch the floor. If she succeeds in doing that she must be praised because of the good position of her legs and feet.

I think that these instructions are sufficient for the moment. If there is a new problem or new success Caroline should write about it to us, we will answer her.

The most important aim is still to make Dina use her hands for eating, drinking, dressing, washing, playing and so on. If necessary her mother can help her so that Dina uses her hands in a really meaningful way. She grasps the soap, and learns to soap herself and to wash her hands. The more she uses her hands in different ways the stronger her arms will get, and they will become less spastic. Then she will be able to use her arms better for crawling, too.

Infants may be able to crawl towards something after a relatively short time but this does not mean that there is a rule that they have to learn crawling before walking. It seems that this is Caroline's own opinion.

Caroline must take care that the hands are in the right position when gripping (wrists!), and that, if necessary, the arms are entirely stretched. For this purpose she gives the minimal necessary help...

13 June 1986

Postscript to the preceding letter to Eva Galla:

Yesterday we forgot to answer the questions about sitting. It is better not to let Dina sit on the floor for a long time, as sitting there is more difficult than on a chair.

When sitting on a chair it is very important that Dina's soles (and heels) are flat on the floor. Caroline should accompany this by saying: "I put my feet flat on the floor". If the plinth is used as a table, Dina can hold herself on it. Caroline may also fasten a rubber band between two slats so that Dina can hold it with one hand and do something with the other.

She has to watch whether Dina falls just to one side when sitting or to both sides. If the former is the case, a chair with the back towards her is put at her side to keep her from falling. A chair with arms should never be used as the arms cannot be taken away later on!

When sitting is taught it should always be connected with a purpose, for example eating, drinking or playing. When Dina looks at a picture book and someone explains what everything is and what things are called, this will be very important for her (motivation) and so she will learn to sit! Sitting must never be trained for sitting's sake, without such aims. Dina must never be bored when sitting!

When drinking she should support herself on the table with her elbows, when eating or playing she can hold on with one hand. She should be taught to hold on in time if she feels that she is beginning to fall. In this way she will learn to keep her balance.

She is always to be praised when sitting straight. And if she does not sit straight she should be told at once: "I sit straight" so she can correct her posture again.

Notes on the present tasks of life

From the beginning when we first heard about Dina through Frau Galla, we said that we help the parents of motor disordered children without asking for money.

The reason for this is not that we lack material problems. But we are in an age when one can see the value of cooperation even under distorting conditions.

There are very important human-biological tasks that cannot be paid for with money.

If the difficulties of a child with cerebral palsy can be overcome by his mother, there is no fixed price for the mother's efforts. One could calculate by looking at how much money could be saved in hospitals and other services were the cost of personnel and materials for the care of a severely handicapped child to become superfluous.

However, this seems to put value only on the mother's successful cooperation with her child. In addition it goes without saying that every mother occupies herself with her child without getting paid for it - there is nobody to pay her!

The mother's anthropogenic, inductively psychogenetic cooperation that creates her child's personality not only cannot be measured with money, but also there is no generally acknowledged descriptive term for it. So the mother's "instinctive" cooperation, which sets in motion her child's personality development, remains hidden. It is only with motor-disordered children whose development proceeds in slow motion and so becomes recognizable that the mother can (and should) recognize the separate components of her interaction, of her behaviour. This case makes clear that the mother is happy about any bit of help from her child, which is quite obvious to spectators as well. The mother's happiness, triggered by the child, makes the child learn to be independent.

Under normal conditions this human-biological cooperation between mother and infant enables rapid development of the child's relationships. There is no concept for this, however, in everyday language.

Thanks to some ethologists, these human-biological relations are beginning to be understood - at least partly - by science.

We tried to prevent the real tasks awaiting Caroline Seiffer in overcoming Dina's difficulties from becoming inappropriate or misleading ones, otherwise Dina's difficulties would not be solved at all. This is another reason why we should not work for money. We want to (and should) keep our powers of judgement independent from everything that might undermine our purpose, so that we can do only what is necessary and justifiable.

The real tasks of life make demands. Their solution not only brings joy but also creates new situations with new tasks. This makes life really interesting and meaningful.

Petö used to say: "Our duty is to whatever the day may bring."

In this case the day brought us (through Eva Galla) the following duty:

She came to see us in Budapest and showed us photographs of two German girls and their doctors' reports. Both are severely motor disordered, one is fourteen years old, the other about the same age as Dina.

The older girl has long outgrown the dual mother-child relationship. She has had seven orthopaedic operations and her condition would not permit any hope for overcoming her difficulties entirely. To improve she would have to be treated in the Petö Institute for years; so we advised the mother to write to the Institute.

In this girl's case we think the mother will not be able to give the necessary help.

We advised the mother of the other girl, who is two and a half, to follow Caroline Seiffer's example, in spite of the doc-

tor's report that says that this child, who is paralysed in both arms and legs, might at the very best be able to drive a wheelchair one day. If the mother educates her child according to the Petö System, with a great deal of effort she may succeed in helping her child to overcome her difficulties and become healthy.

We assume that she will follow our advice. We thought this would demand that we give a sort of summary for those mothers who want to help their handicapped children using the Petö System. This is why the booklet that introduces this book was written.

2 August 1986

To Eva Galla:

...We enclose a booklet necessary for Dina's further development and which will help Caroline to support other mothers with similar problems.

Continuation of the above note

At that time we wrote in the booklet: "How can a young mother oppose expert opinions, institutions and authorities? We think she should ask those mothers who healed their children with the Petö System for advice, or at least those who have made good progress. In this case the mothers should help each other without regard to bureaucratic institutions and material interests. Through this booklet we hope to support this."

This is what we wrote then, and it continued:

"The story goes that the King wanted to reward the inventor of chess. This man asked for the following: for the first square on the chessboard he wanted to have one wheatcorn, for the second square two corns, for the third square four corns, then eight and so on. This wish seemed to be very modest. But when the king wanted to fulfil it he had to realize that the amount of the constantly doubling corns was more than all the wheat that he possessed.

If every mother who succeeds with Conductive Education supports only two other mothers, helps them with their decisions and gives them advice, then this problem of motor disorder, which is so overwhelming today, will soon diminish."

When Eva Galla brought us together with Dina's mother and when we began to support her, we did not foresee that this could give us a chance to alter the situation of motor-disordered people generally.

This shows that in biology the realistic solution of problems may often bring along new and astonishing possibilities. We chose our quotation from Faust with regard to the hidden and unexpected possibilities which exist but are not used in our time. Mothers will only discover them through long and intensive activity with their children.

13 August 1986

From Caroline Seiffer:

Our journey to Budapest is definitely planned. We will arrive at the airport in the evening of 15th September. As Eva already told you, we want to have a consultation the next morning ...

In the afternoon we will come to your home to have a talk.

Frau Gross will accompany us with her little daughter Steffi. I think Eva has already shown you the reports. The mother is now really hopeful. The mother of the other girl (Silke, fourteen years old) has written to Dr Hári. The girl herself wants to be treated there.

Eva told me about your booklet, which she is just translating. I think that it is a really wonderful idea. As soon as the translation is done I will type it out and offer it to a publishing house. We have a big monthly magazine for parents which covers all problems and difficulties that can arise with children. It has a special page for parents with handicapped children. I wrote to this magazine, asking them whether they are interested. You may then get an inquiry about permission for publication.

Note on the objective problems of motor-disordered children in the FRG

Schlack [1](1971) says that the number of children with cerebral palsy is two to three in every 1000 live births.

In 1987 the "Bundesverband für spastisch Gelähmte und andere Körperbehinderte" (the "Spastics Society") put the number of spastically paralysed people under eighteen years at 50,000. Three to four of every 1000 newborn are spastic.

This can give us an idea of the objective situation. A huge part of the population is affected.

I only have one question: Should Dina and I go to the group sessions for just two hours in the morning as we did the last time or should we stay there the whole day this time? What would you say to that?...

In July we went for a three-weeks' holiday to Lake Constance and whilst there we could not do all our exercises in the normal way, which was very good, however. We had to improvise. Dina did not pull herself up at the wall bars but on chairs. She is very good at pulling herself up with her arms although her legs cannot keep up with them, they have to be corrected. Walking just now is not so interesting for Dina, she wants to be occupied with toys, particularly recognizing toys. She loves being asked where something is, she points out the right things most of the time, not with one finger but with the whole hand.

People always tell me that they think Dina can understand everything, but that she answers in her own language. She talks a lot, in a special voice and accent. She is now able to hold pieces of bread or sausage in her hand and take a bite from them. She lets me feed her with the spoon but does not hold it herself.

1   Schlack, Hans G., in *Sandorama* 1971/II, p. 11

Dina can sit in her pram quite freely now and holds on to the sides of it. She can sit for a short time on her little chair with the handles. She can even sit on the floor, supporting herself. She did not fall over whilst I counted to fifty.

Now we are practising something new. I hold Dina with one hand under her tummy and she supports herself with both hands and moves forward on her hands and knees alternately. She enjoys it very much and I think that this is great progress. Up to now she stretched her legs out stiffly and did not want to support herself with her arms.

I realize now how important it is to talk constantly to Dina, she reacts wonderfully. We will show and tell you everything else when we come to see you.

25 August 1986

To Eva Galla:

Today we received Caroline's letter dated August 13th.

The letter contains just one question which we want to answer here, so I do not have to write in German and can write to you in Hungarian.

We could see from Caroline's letter that you have not only received the material but have also told her about it and are busy translating it. We are glad to hear that. I hope you do not have too much trouble with the translation. If any questions arise just write to us.

Caroline asked us how long she should stay in the Institute each day. The answer is: the whole day if possible. It is important that both of them have as much experience as possible. Caroline will see from other children which tasks and possible solutions there are in various situations (eating, sitting on the potty, washing and especially playing). Dina will surely show interest in the other children.

Caroline had only good news to tell about Dina. This means that her personality development is going well.

Sometimes Caroline is uncertain about her educational activity. She is right in saying that walking now is no longer a central aim for Dina, in contrast to the times when she thought that it was. In reality even then it was only the means to get somewhere where she wanted to be. Dina did not start walking because she wanted to walk but because she wanted to go to the playground. Caroline could move Dina's feet for all eternity; she would never start walking on her own. For example, even if she had to go to the dentist she would not have been able to do so.

So one should never put food, drinks, or toys simply in front of a child who can walk and is hungry, thirsty, or wants to play. The things that the child wants should be at a distance that the child can manage. In this way she will learn to walk.

Caroline has not yet realized that sitting on the floor is more difficult than sitting on a chair that stands in front of a table (plinth) where Dina can hold on. She cannot do that on the floor and there her legs do not support her body. But when the child wants to play with something on the table she will learn to sit by holding on with one hand and reaching for her goal (the toy) with the other. A game is played with this aim.

The mother must always be careful that Dina sits straight, thus preventing scoliosis. Sitting straight on the floor is especially difficult.

Caroline described how skilfully she made up a crawling game. It is very good that Dina already uses her arms and legs for that. For this game as well Dina needs a goal that she can go towards.

In the booklet we sent you it is exactly these issues that are discussed in detail.

We look forward to seeing Caroline, Dina and also Steffi and her mother...

12 August 1986

From Eva Galla:

I received your manuscript...At the moment I have not got time for translating, not even for thorough reading...

Caroline and the other mother have already bought their tickets and will arrive as planned.

Caroline told me that Dina is developing well. Lately she has not improved as quickly as she did with her walking, but she does make advances slowly but surely. She babbles a lot now, so Caroline expects her to start speaking soon.

Caroline is no industrious letter-writer but she has two other children and has to look after a house all by herself, which she does like any other housewife, with typical German thoroughness. She is rather exhausted. She has not slept through one single night since Dina's birth as Dina used to wake up several times and she still does so, at least once a night.

The mother of the fourteen-year-old girl wrote to the Institute and hopes that she will be accepted.

19 August 1986

From Eva Galla:

I started translating on Sunday morning and was so fascinated by the booklet that I worked the whole day long till after midnight! I only had breaks for eating and yoga exercises against the pain in my arms and shoulders. But I just could not stop, I liked it so much. However, at midnight I was so tired that I had to stop before finishing the last three pages, and finished it on Monday morning. Because of the excessive writing I can hardly feel my right side, but I wanted to write this letter.

I have some questions:

- What does "temporal and intercerebral brain function" mean?

- How does the "mechanism of the development of consciousness" work?

-What do you mean by "relational psychology"?

These questions are from the section on the authors. Please explain them to me as I cannot translate what I cannot understand. If I try a literal translation it always ends up as nonsense. And what I, a qualified educationalist, cannot understand will most probably not be understood by the mothers for whom this is intended.

Besides, I am already so far into the practical side of Conductive Education that now I want to know more about the theoretical aspects.

Not long ago we talked about psychochronography, but I did not understand much about it. Maybe I could understand better now. But you must not forget that I am no specialist and that you should therefore not use specialists' terms.

Just as I had many problems with the first section, the text that follows was easy to translate. Everything is clear, logical and wonderfully simple!

Caroline will come to my house on Sunday and we will read the booklet together...

29 August 1986

To Eva Galla:

...We very much enjoyed your last letter expressing your enthusiasm about our booklet. This convinces us that mothers will be able to benefit from it...

The part about the authors is only meant to provide a little information. It was not written to tell the mothers what we are doing but to give them information in case specialists ask "who are these Akos people..."

Here are some explanations:

By "general brain function" we mean the function of the brain as a whole and not the function of its parts. Brain research can be done in two ways. One method studies general functions by comparing input and output. The other tries to explain partial functions with regard to certain structures in the brain. We think, however, that the structure of the brain is enormously complicated (a "black box"). This makes it impossible to understand its general function on the basis of the partial functions. But it is possible to examine the conditions that may influence and change the behaviour of the personality.

We discovered that specifically human-biological, intercerebral (= between two or more brains) cooperation is of fundamental importance for the functional changes in the human brain which manifest themselves as personality. Personality can be defined as the brain's function in an "intercerebral field". This must not be confused with so-called "extrasensory perception". The intercerebral field is totally real, an interplay between physiological factors of cooperation, as for example language, common activities and so on. Personality develops because of changes of the brain functions, which in the human-biological sense come into existence through learning in a changing "intercerebral field".

When we look at the mother and child we find that the "intercerebral field" consists almost exclusively of mutual cooperation. Thus the child's personality development happens in a cooperative, educational interrelationship between mother and child. The mother relates to the child in such a way as to learn from him which form of cooperation he needs and, at the same time, to teach him to cooperate more and more with her. This way he will contribute more and more to "helping" his mother to solve his problems, and will gradually become more independent. This is personality development.

A child with brain damage is hindered by the symptoms of damage from giving those signals to his mother which are necessary for the mother's appropriate response. Therefore the mother cannot teach her child correctly and he cannot learn. He will remain motor-disordered.

If, however, a mother can get help and instructions in this situation appropriate intercerebral cooperation becomes possible and those relationships necessary for the child's personality development are initiated. This "anthropogenic cooperation" not only influences the child's behaviour in a positive way but also eventually diminishes the symptoms of brain damage.

This is the theoretical explanation for the success of the Pető System during the first years of a child's life.

Later on the "intercerebral field" which was first confined to the mother, and less so to the other members of the family, will expand gradually, first to the other members of the family, then mainly to children of about the same age. (The conductors purposely use the "intercerebral field" of the group to achieve the personality development which enables difficulties to be overcome.)

The brain function which manifests itself as personality not only shows itself in the activities of an individual but also in language. We showed that individual consciousness develops from passive (coming from somebody) and active (directed to somebody) language. A child learns to speak through cooperative interrelationship with his mother.

Because of the general function of the brain, which works with feedback control systems - or as von Holst[1] more correctly says: is "reafferent" - consciousness develops alongside the learning of language, as long as the mother teaches her child not just to verbalise but also to internalise what is experienced. This way the child will learn inner language, and so consciousness will develop.

Now we come to "psychochronography".

The general way in which a brain functions consists of processing information (input) from both the inner (within the body) and outer environments, followed by the organization of output (the reaction to the input).

[1]   von Holst, E. and Mittelstaedt, H. M., Das Reafferenzprinzip, in: Naturwissenschaften, 37, 1950, pp. 464-476

But all changes depend on time, they are temporal, and so overall brain activity is also bound to time. This means that brain function, when receiving repeated, similar information, will specifically change because of each of these repetitions; the most recent information (input) changes the starting point for the next. This change can be seen in the output.

Central fatigue is characterized by a change in brain function, caused by a series of repeated, identical inputs. A break interrupting this series diminishes the amount of central fatigue.

In psychochronography (PCG) an identical perception (output!) changes during its repetition. This change is quantitatively defined through change in the amount of the physical input, which is always necessary for the appearance of psychological output. The change of the quantity of relaxation (regeneration) is measured by the repetition of identical breaks. So there are quantitative input-output relations which enable us to verify certain rules about changes of functions in the brain and to discover their initial conditions.

This is the shortest description of psychochronography.

The term "relational psychology" means that personality, as a general brain function of the individual, develops under specific human-biological conditions in connection with other personalities.

We only answered your questions very roughly. If there are further questions please ask them, we will be glad to answer...

20 September 1986

To Eva Galla:

The two mothers came to see us with their children on 19 September.

They go to the Institute regularly and will come to our house again the day after tomorrow.

We are writing to you now to give further advice to Caroline, and to give you enough time to translate it before they are home again.

Dina has made obvious progress in her overall personality development since March, thanks to her mother's efforts. How can Caroline develop these achievements further?

A. Opportunities for correction
Eating, chewing, talking
When Caroline takes Dina on her lap she should do this in such a way that the child can see and observe her face (facial expression and especially movements of the mouth). This is also important for Dina when sitting at the table and eating.

Children like to imitate their mother's movements of the mouth. Dina must learn to close her lips properly when chewing and swallowing. Her mother opens and closes her own lips at the same time and this will show Dina the right position. Each bite is accompanied by words: "I open my mouth", "I shut it", "I chew", "I swallow"... In this way Dina will learn to keep her food in her mouth, to chew strongly, to swallow consciously, and to swallow her saliva as well. From time to time Caroline can show how she herself eats and how she keeps her lips closed when chewing. To help Dina's understanding now and then she can also close her child's lips with her hands or support the movements of the lower jaw when chewing. If Dina's lips open when eating, the mother can say: "Keep your mouth tightly shut. Don't let the food fall out!" Later on it will suffice to say: "I shut my mouth."

As soon as Dina is able to shut her mouth properly and chew on her own, she will no longer need this "verbal intention".

To learn to chew, solid food is better than mashed food or liquids.

Dina has already started to answer with sounds when her mother sits opposite her and talks to her. She should often be talked to in this way. To learn to eat and to chew will also help her ability to articulate.

If Caroline can guess from Dina's behaviour what she wants to express when she "speaks", Caroline should repeat these words correctly and then fulfil her wishes.

When Dina looks into her mother's face, Caroline should make her expression more vivid. If Dina's look changes, Caroline should imitate it and put its meaning into words. For example if Dina laughs, Caroline should laugh as well and say: "You are laughing, you're in a good mood." If Dina is in a bad mood, Caroline should imitate this as well and say: "So you're in a bad mood, I suppose you are angry about something."

When talking to Dina Caroline should exaggerate the movements of her mouth a bit, she should articulate clearly and pronounce the words slowly, slightly lengthening the vowels.

Caroline's singing and telling stories to Dina is part of the process of learning to speak. She should do this loud and strong, accompanied by facial expressions and gestures. Dina will be motivated to join in. Clapping hands, showing what is being talked about, lifting her arms, legs and feet and so on. As far as possible the contents of the stories and songs should relate to the child's own experiences and feelings and to the things she sees and does.

Tendency to fall backwards

Dina's spastic tendency that makes her extend her head backwards needs to be counteracted before this gets worse and she starts falling backwards. Her mother should sit in front of Dina as often as possible to make her look forward, stretch her arms forward and bend forward. When Dina's head stretches backwards she must not, for example, be kissed as the tendency to adopt this posture will then be rewarded and strengthened.

B. Using the time

Teaching gripping

Dina should be fed slowly with little breaks in between mouthfuls, so that she gets more time to take part in this and do something on her own. This may lead her to find that she can lift the spoon or cup. Her mother should encourage this progress verbally, by praising Dina and thereby making conscious the new movements.

Caroline should always encourage Dina to join in the activity and praise her cooperation.

Dina should also be encouraged in this way when she changes her position on the plinth or her posture by gripping, or when she uses either both her hands or each hand alternately when playing. Such games should not only be encouraged but also initiated and developed further.

The more time that is used for playful and cooperative activity with the child each day, the less time will be needed for her to recover fully.

Dina should actually use everything that she has already learned. Nothing should be done for her which she could do on her own, provided that she is not ill or tired.

Teaching walking

The mother constantly needs to find new goals which will motivate Dina to walk, and which she can achieve using her own strength, even if she needs help at first.

The distance that Dina can walk will have to be increased gradually. When Dina is able to achieve an aim - even if very slowly - she must never be carried to that object to save time, as this will hinder the process of learning to walk.

1 October 1986

To Eva Galla:

Yesterday both the mothers and their children were here. Tomorrow they will go back home again.

Our impression of the children was a very good one. Dina uses her hands much better than even a week ago and the child has become more physically relaxed and active. (This does not, however, invalidate our last letter.) Caroline thinks that she has learned a great deal at the Institute although everything went on too fast, which the children did not like.

We did not previously know Steffi, the other girl, nor do we know what her condition was like before her mother began to treat her according to Petö, at the time when her mother first contacted Caroline.

When we met Steffi for the first time she was able to use her hands quite well for eating, although she splayed her fingers too much. She is generally very dexterous with her hands. She needs very little help for eating. She brought a doll and took off its clothes - with a lot of encouragement from her mother.

However, she was not yet able to sit without her mother's help, and she could not take a single step. Yesterday she took many little steps when she was taken by the hands, but she does not lift her knees and her feet shuffle on the floor. However, she is able to push them forward on her own. Her arms are bent.

She was able to speak five words; yesterday she said the sixth - "Dina". The two girls seemed to be very interested in each other.

We suggested to the mothers a monthly meeting, together with the children. The girls should eat and play, and solve their "tasks" together. One child should go to the other and bring some toy or take it ("Please-Thank-you-game") and so on. The mothers should discuss their problems and achievements together. Like this two goals are aimed for, which we will now explain further as your assistance might be necessary if the mothers have any questions.

1. The children are at an age when they start to grow out of the mutual relationship with their mothers and need cooperation with a group of children of the same age. (The children's personality development depends on such cooperation.)

For example, their strong motivation to relate to each other can be seen clearly in Steffi's rapid learning of Dina's name. As the level of the two children's achievement is relatively low and they are therefore not able to cooperate well with healthy children, it is not advisable to let them go to a regular kindergarten. For their personality development, however, they need contact with other children of the same age (children learn a lot from each other by imitating). This is much more important, as they have to catch up on the development of healthy children.

2. The mothers' cooperation is important to speed up the process of overcoming their children's difficulties. Even under "normal" circumstances a mother will not only influence her own child with her educational activity but she will also give an example to other mothers. However, this influence does not usually take place consciously.

Motor-disordered children do not guide their mothers sufficiently. This makes the mothers' education more difficult and hinders the child's development.

It is the essence of mother-centred Conductive Education to lead the mother to conscious recognition of her educational tasks. This also means that she has to be aware of the importance of details and measures which are normally hidden but which are necessary for achieving aims, for actual practice. If the mother realizes this she will be able to contribute successfully to her infant's personality development and the early difficulties can be overcome.

As the two mothers only get the necessary instruction in writing and from two-week stays twice a year in the Petö Institute, they have to give each other the support which we could give them and their children if we were able to meet, for example once a month. We propose that they should meet once or twice a month, carefully discuss their problems and take our booklet with its practical instructions for help.

The two girls have somewhat different problems. This is an advantage, as one mother might be able to find more easily a solution for the problem of the other child. With regard to Caroline we have already discovered that she is capable of finding the interactions necessary for Dina's personality development. Steffi's mother too has fully understood the meaning of "anthropogenic cooperation" and can use it practically. Now she is to get the booklet from Caroline that you translated.

This booklet is also an important source of support against the inevitable resistance of specialists. It is meant to help the mothers undertake their activity as intensively as possible, without being confused by others. Steffi's mother has also received a letter from us with summarized instructions.

At this point we realized that we had stirred up a positive hornet's nest with our mothers' use of the Petö System for overcoming the difficulties of children with cerebral palsy, as now there would be more and more mothers coming to get help for their children.

19 October 1986

From Caroline Seiffer:

Dina and I arrived home well, as did Frau Gross and Steffi. We parted in Munich but she will come to see us next week.

Your booklet is ready and I will send you a copy. I am afraid that as yet there is no publisher who wants it. But some copies are already circulating. One copy went to a young doctor in L. whom I had to go to see with Dina. She was very open to your method. Of course she had not known it before and she advised me to follow your instructions. She wanted to learn more about it so I sent her a copy. She only treats motor-disordered children and may be able to recommend your methods.

In the meantime Dina and I got used to our new workload. We work intensively a few hours each morning and it is going quite well. There is nothing new yet to tell you but I can safely say that her balance is becoming more stable. She sits on her potty all on her own without being held and generally she is trying to support herself when sitting.

Frau Gross is pleased as well. We will give you a report when she comes to see us at the end of the month.

1 November 1986

To Eva Galla:

Caroline's letter with your translation of our booklet has arrived. The translation is done very well, but one misunderstanding appears again and again. It is about the position of the infant's wrist. We wrote that the mother should press the wrist slightly backwards, towards the back of the hand, with her forefinger positioned to prevent bending of the hand forward towards the palm. Somehow it has to be made clear what forward (towards the palm) and backward (towards the back of the hand) mean. Anatomists call them palmar and dorsal movements, but our everyday language is not so definite.

We are sending you a picture page from our book about relational psychology, *The Meaning of Human Life*, containing four pictures of a child. You can see the spastic bending in the third photo. The second picture shows the same symptoms in the feet. It would be advisable for Caroline to give a copy of these pictures to everyone who gets a booklet...(see photos on the following pages)

By the way Caroline is right in thinking that it is more important now to give the booklet to others than to wait for a publisher. The main thing is to help the "mothers' movement", the publishers will follow some time.

We were very glad to hear that Dina can keep her balance when sitting and that Frau Gross is pleased with Steffi's development. Meanwhile she should have visited Caroline. We are waiting eagerly for the first report about the mothers-and-children meeting and the results...

It was also very interesting that the specialist in L. is curious about our method...

In November I will participate in an international scientific conference in Washington. The spiritual supporter of this conference is the Hungarian-American Nobel Prize winner of physics, Eugen P. Wigner. The special thing about my invitation is the fact that I was asked to give a commentary to the lecture of two Australian scientists. They talk about ethical problems in relation to infants with severe congenital damage and whether it is right to let these children live or whether it would be better to let them die. They support the latter and mainly base their reasoning on the idea that newborn infants do not yet have a "personality". If they had said "soul" instead of "personality" immediately there would have been a fierce debate between themselves and the theologians. But they could not explain how a healthy infant develops a personality.

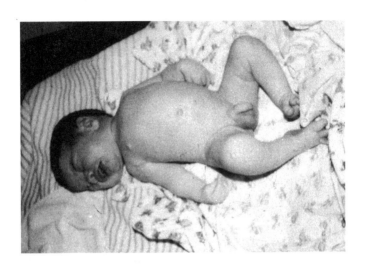

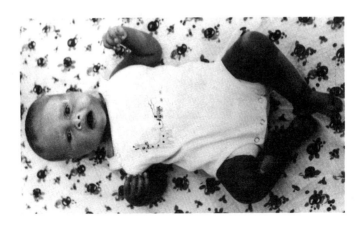

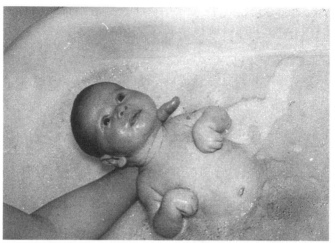

"Tibi" from the book by Akos and Akos *The Meaning of Human Life*
(Relational Psychology).
The first three pictures show the early, severe symptoms of a boy with
tetraplegic cerebral palsy.
The fourth picture shows the boy running. He no longer shows symptoms.
Many years have passed since then. Tibi goes to a normal school and is an
excellent pupil. He shows no differences from children of the same age.
However, a scoliosis could not be prevented.

I will show with the example of children with cerebral palsy that a child's personality develops from the cooperative, educational interrelationship between the child and his mother.

These Australian scientists make no distinction between children with severe cerebral palsy and others with severe congenital damage. They hold the idea that there is no hope of improvement for either group. But we want to show that there is a possibility that motor-disordered infants can overcome their difficulties.

This hope does not come from medicine, nor from public health services, but from their mothers. The social problem of cerebral palsy is by no means smaller than that of, for example, cancer. The number of people with cancer in the whole world is about the same as that of people with motor disorders.

Would it not be fantastic if the worldwide problem of motor-disordered children could be solved by their mothers?

8 November 1986

From Caroline Seiffer:

Here is the promised report about the visit of Susanne Gross and Steffi. It is wonderful that we will meet regularly now as we got on very well together in Budapest and we can talk about our problems easily. Besides, Dina and Steffi were glad to meet again.

Susanne is very pleased with Steffi's development. It seems that Steffi works quite well with her and she can see progress in her balance. When lying on the floor she plays nicely but she does not crawl forward, or at least does so seldom and only a little. Susanne says that Steffi is "lazy".

Caroline Seiffer now reports about Steffi's development and encouragement by the mother.

Now about Dina.

Note on the cooperation between the mothers.

It is very interesting that a mother reports first about the child of another mother and then about her own. It is not that she is uninterested in her own child. Frau Seiffer realized that cooperation between two mothers and their children is the common factor for this group. That is why Steffi's progress is so important to her. Frau Seiffer fears that Steffi's mother is not yet confident enough in developing her educational abilities to the maximum. But she can see quite clearly that this cannot be forced. What was said about the children is also true for the mothers. The right support in both cases consists of finding situations in which spontaneous learning is possible. Caroline can well remember that earlier she had not always been able to judge Dina's situation properly and to find the right ways of doing things. We had to make clear to her the reasons for the resistance to effective interaction between herself and Dina, which was not easy. Now that she has recognized this and is looking about for ways of motivating the other mother to cooperate, she can see how great the problems are. She will learn that it is best to wait until the mother gets the necessary hints through Steffi's behaviour, as her own child is the best means of motivation for a mother.

Also the motor disorder of the two children is not the same. The main direction in Dina's education for independence is change of position, by recognizing her surroundings as something worth seeing, as a visual object.

Steffi's world is more tangible, perceptible, something to touch.

Each mother should adapt herself to her child, that is why these two are able to complement one another. Caroline is the more experienced 'sister', better able to express her doubts. But earlier it was hard for her, too, to recognize and articulate her difficulties.

Both Dina's and Steffi's stability increase more and more. Dina now sits on a little stool in front of the seat of a bigger chair, and plays on it. I have to be near her as sometimes she is likely to fall over when she plays with her hands and stops holding on. This way of sitting is quite new and only started when we returned from Budapest. She often has her back bent but when I tell her to sit straight she sits up on her own and keeps upright for some time.

She can walk with the chair now, by holding on to the rungs. I only support her legs a bit, as she crosses them sometimes. In this way we can walk across the room, about six-and-a-half metres. After a little rest we go back again. In addition to that we practise walking sideways along the bed each day. I have to help her but her legs open quite easily, which used to be hard work only a few weeks ago. We let a car run along the bed and then go and get it again by walking along the bed. It is a funny game for Dina!

Eating on her own still is a problem. Dina is now so clever that when I want to put the spoon to her mouth she rejects it and "tells" me by sounds and looks that I should eat the food myself. She only opens her mouth when I feed her. One day I just put down the spoon and told her she had to eat on her own as I was busy. I sat at the table and did something else and at first Dina did nothing at all. She just mumbled a bit because she was hungry. After a short time she had the spoon in her hand and tried to put food on it. She actually succeeded to get something into her mouth and we all praised her very much. Since then it has become better, as has drinking from a mug.

Stretching her arms has improved a great deal. She can lift her arms up without help and stretch them and clap, for example "Pat-a-cake, Pat-a-cake...", but she still clenches her fists.

Note on an educational mistake.

At first Caroline used the song "Pat-a-cake, pat-a-cake..." together with learning to grip. Doing this Dina grasped her mother's forefingers with both her hands. The mother moved the little fists together and apart again. In this game the child's hands were of course clenched.

But when Dina claps her hands above her head her hands should be open. So it can be confusing when the song that was used together with closing the fist is now used in a different context.

In the child's brain function the movements are combined in a common pattern of activity (game) with the language and the rhythm and therefore should always occur together.

She does not speak yet but she indicates more frequently the things that she wants to have or do, and is generally more interested. Unfortunately she gets very angry when we do not understand her or when she does not get what she wants. Then she throws herself backwards and screams.

There are also advances in playing. She now is able to roll a ball, to give it to her fellow player.

You can see that I am very pleased and am always told by friends that Dina is making good progress.

Now I have to tell you something very interesting.

Susanne Gross lives near H. About three weeks ago there was a lecture in the 'Diakonische Werke' about the Petö method from Budapest!!! The talk had been initiated by the "Institute for the Integration of Spastics" in Vienna, by a Frau Helga Keil and a Frau Nalis, who were looking for people interested in a course in Vienna in Summer 87, where the Petö method could be learned.

It is a pity Frau Gross did not hear about it until three days after it happened, and then only because one of her neighbours heard and realized that it might well be the same as what Frau Gross had told him about.

Susanne contacted the 'Diakonische Werke' and they are now thinking about inviting you to H. to talk there. My task now is to ask you if you would agree in principle to such a journey. I think that there would be a lot of people interested because I have been asked again and again why this method is not known here.

I will go on circulating your booklet. In a periodical for parents of handicapped children I found the letter of a single father who has a four-year-old spastic child already able to walk alone holding on to furniture but not making any further progress. This father wanted to know whether there were any other parents who are not content with our usual methods such as Bobath and Vojta and with the way in which people are treated by therapists and specialists. I will write to this father and send him a copy. Maybe he will find it helpful too.

You see there is plenty going on here.

Now something else, although I do not know whether you can help me with it. In the Institute I asked for a certificate that Dina had been an out-patient there and I got it. Now our health insurance asks for another certificate which must say that the Institute is directed by a physician and that it is the only Institute of this kind in Europe. I wrote to Frau Dr Hári and only got another one which says that Dina was an out-patient.

I am afraid this will not suffice for eventually getting the costs refunded. Maybe you can see a way to help me to get it.

In the next few days I will go to Eva and we will look at your letter together.

9 November 1986

From Eva Galla:

...Yesterday evening Caroline was here and I informed her about your letter.

The quotation is on the front page of the booklet. I think it is very good. The German title is: "How can a mother restore the health of her motor-disordered infant?"

Caroline wants to ask you a favour. The health insurance rejected her application for refunding the costs for the flight because they think that Budapest is not the nearest place of treatment for Dina. So Caroline wrote to the Institute asking for a certificate saying that there is no other such institute in Europe. She got the enclosed certificate.

The certificate was enclosed in the letter. The diagnosis was: "Tetraparesis spastica", that means "incomplete paralysis of the four extremities".

Caroline, however, needs the certificate that I described above. Maybe Magdi could explain it at the Institute and get it for Caroline. *(Magdi is one of our daughters, who works in the Petö Institute as a conductor.)*

I wish you lots of success in Washington for your debate with the Australians.

In this context I have a question. What exactly do you mean by "personality"? This is a question that often arises during the translation. It is clear that everything depends on personality development but what are we supposed to understand by it?

20 November 1986

To Eva Galla:

We were very glad about the letters from you and from Caroline; nevertheless they brought some new tasks with them.

Your question about personality could only really be answered in a book. In spite of that we will try to give a summary that is as short as possible.

We believe that apart from a congenital (physiological) brain function there is another one; this human-biological function is built upon the physiological one from the instant of birth. The human-biological changes of brain function develop in cooperation with other brains (intercerebral). So personality originates and develops in "anthropogenic cooperation" between personalities in a group. This is the reason for forming groups.

These connections are hard to conceptualise within our system of thinking and thus cannot be understood easily.

The usual conventional concepts give us the impression that they are natural and this hinders changing them. Obscurities, contradictions and boundaries are not realized, and the idea of necessary new definitions does not arise at all.

This is the reason why we will try to be more concrete.

When I met Petö in the year 1946, my wife and I had already done research about the general function of the brain. During the following years we defined the course of the development of individual consciousness. We were very interested from the viewpoint of theory in Petö's apparently inexplicable success. He himself did not explain it theoretically; he did not think much about theories as he was mainly interested in healing patients.

Even at the time that I wrote the book Hári/Akos *Conductive Education* we (my wife and I) knew no more than that Conductive Education mobilizes the unused functional reserves of the brain.

It was more then ten years later that we learned what are the necessary conditions for mobilizing the last reserves of the brain...

Everybody is ready for interaction from birth onwards. The mother solves her child's problems because first she is activated by his crying and then she cooperates with him. This not only solves the problem but also makes the child join in the cooperative effort.

The mother's joy at his response further strengthens this behaviour.

As the child cooperates more and more with his mother, he learns to contribute more to the solving of his problems and thus becomes more independent. Therefore his independence is a result of this cooperation with his mother. His ability for cooperation increases and through his "guidance" that of the mother increases too. A newborn child is already able to make his mother understand through his behaviour whether his problem is solved or not.

The child's personality develops from this "cooperative educational interrelationship". The infant becomes more and more independent, more able to recognize and use the necessary conditions for the solving of a problem (which is what is meant by "orientation") and to increase his mother's ability for interaction with him.

In favourable circumstances the personality development that started in infancy will carry on for life, but it may also get stuck or take a wrong direction.

Here we talk only about the personality development of the infant, which develops out of the cooperation of two brains (in the form of activities and language). This cooperation gets stuck if the mother does not receive the necessary guidance from her child's behaviour. Then there is no educational influence from the mother, necessary for the human-biological changes in physiological brain function. This is the reason why this child then becomes a severe case of cerebral palsy. At first the brain damage itself causes only relatively slight disturbances of the physiological brain function. Those functions that are necessary for living are not disordered. The severe symptoms of a cerebral palsy are not caused directly by the brain damage, as one can often read in specialist literature, but are only secondary. The mother did not receive the guidance from her infant that is necessary for his personality development, for increasing his ability to cooperate. If the mother is helped to realize how she can increase her child's cooperation, which is at first rather weak, then with relatively few instructions she can also learn how to increase his ability to cooperate more and more. So the child's retarded personality development is restarted. At the same time the mother can teach her child - as a sort of by-product - to overcome the brain damage symptoms and so become healthy.

In spite of the increased difficulties for cooperation in the teaching and learning process between a mother and her motor-disordered child, once restored "intercerebral cooperation" is essentially the same as with a healthy child. Only the mother has to do in a conscious way that which happens spontaneously in a healthy child, especially with regard to individual problems which usually remain unconscious.

However, this is not the mother's greatest problem. Her greatest problem is the instruction which she needs but at present does not usually receive. On the contrary, the mother often receives information which scares her, puts her on the wrong track and prevents her from finding solutions by her own efforts, although she might be able to do so to a high degree. As a consequence her child's personality remains at the infant level.

When that child reaches an age when he needs not only his mother but also a group of children of the same age, he will already have more severe symptoms. It would take longer to correct these, and it would be necessary to stay in the Petö Institute the whole day. There the conductor supports the child's ability to interact with the children in the group. She satisfies the needs of the children, initiates and supports their ability for cooperation and is guided by her observations just as the mother is with her infant.

You have seen that first we had to encourage Caroline to stop superfluous, torturing, forced and passive gymastics so that she could learn to adapt her educational aims to her child's aims (motivation).

Then it was not absolutely necessary to explain to her that there would be a cooperative educational interrelationship between Dina and herself, an "intercerebral field" between the two brain functions, and that this was the way for Dina to develop her personality. Caroline became able to master her human-biological, educational task just like any mother, through the good environment, the activity, and the help that she was able to give increasingly to her child. She realized the difference that it makes for a child who is thirsty to get something to drink from her mother or to drink something on his own, with only such help as is absolutely necessary. It is difficult to understand the meaning of the gradual change in the educational process which makes human-biological modification of the child's brain function possible.

This becomes clearer - in relation to a concrete situation - when you read our letter to Caroline.

Dear Caroline!

We are very glad about our collaboration with you as you begin to understand so well your tasks for overcoming Dina's difficulties. That is why your daughter develops so well. For example, Dina can stand at the window for some time because you succeeded in motivating her to stand there because of the things that go on outside. Here you have not only taught her to stand but also to use her hands. Most probably you show her the things she can see and tell her the names, and in this way she will learn to differentiate things visually and to understand language. The more educational aims that you are able to combine, the faster Dina's physical and psychological development will proceed.

Now you should try to get to the stage where she herself points out what she can see. Then she will not only learn to recognize and name the things that she has seen, but also to stand while holding on with one hand and to talk. If you give her a ring, a doll or some other toy in one hand, and try to make her point at something on the street with her other hand, she will stand without holding on and at the same time use her hands in differentiated ways. Of course you will have to take care that she does not fall over, similarly when she is sitting.

Gradually building up partial aims has a central meaning in educational activity. For example, this has taught Dina to eat with a spoon on her own. First she helped you more and more with feeding and so became more independent. In the end, to her own astonishment, she could bring the spoon to her mouth alone. The fact was that she was left alone when eating and the motivation of the sight of the food (hunger) mobilized the things learned before. As you properly recognized this must be developed further. Only help her when she is obviously too tired to go on eating alone.

The anger and defiance that Dina now shows should not scare you. It is a good sign that she sets herself goals and also has the energy to want to reach them. She is just not always able to use this energy correctly. Her fits of anger should not be supressed. Instead of that you should look for goals that she wants to reach and you should help her to find ways to them, in other words to channel her energy.

There are many possible ways of helping correctly. You can put the thing she wants nearer to her so that she can reach it alone when she stretches her arm. You can turn it so that she can grasp it. You always have to think about things carefully. What can I teach my child on the way to reaching a goal independently? This also gives you an opportunity to make Dina speak, for example by asking her: "Do you want to have that? Yes?" The "yes" should always be accompanied by a nod, at least at first, the "no" with shaking the head. You can demonstrate this to her.

If for example she wants to have the ball, you tell her that she would have got it already, if she had asked for the "ball".

There are many intermediate steps on the way to acquiring language. Dina should chew a lot. She must learn to chew and to swallow her saliva with her mouth closed.

She will learn to blow when playing. You blow in Dina's hand, then you blow into the air and Dina should blow into her own hand. Feeling the air will help her learn to blow. Take a bowl filled with water and put a paper boat on it. She will see that the boat starts moving when she blows it. You can also use a ping-pong ball. If later on she gets a trumpet or flute and learns to blow it, letting out her breath will be connected with hearing. Blow soap-bubbles with her and so on.

Stand in front of Dina often, imitate her facial expressions and encourage her to imitate yours. Open and close your mouth, purse your lips, smile, show your teeth, lick your lips with your tongue. For this you can put some pudding or something similar that she likes on her lips. This may help her understand what she is supposed to do, namely to lick. Sing a lot with her while sitting or standing opposite her so she can see your mouth. Always accompany your activities with words as described in the booklet (cf.Part I).

It is important to remember that cooperation with other people is becoming more and more important for Dina's personality development. The others have to be made aware of their educational tasks as well, directly or indirectly. It is a great advantage that Dina's father already helps! The meetings between Dina and Steffi and their games should also be organized in this way.

This is the reason why it is very important for Susanne Gross to understand what her role is in Steffi's education, what meaning her activity has and what tasks she is facing. Frau Gross does very well with her daughter with regard to learning the use of hands. Using her hands is Steffi's strong point. However, she needs advice on other points. Susanne must learn to recognize her child's problems. For this she needs to be able to talk and write about it in an unrestrained way. She need not be afraid of being a nuisance to you or us with her questions. Real help creates joy which is a reward in itself. If she does not ask questions she will not be able to use all her opportunities consciously.

Susanne is a nice woman who cares a lot about her child, but she is a bit timid. Encourage her to write to us if she has trouble.

She will learn that a mother can never be entirely content, because every achievement is only a step to the next. Of course one has every reason to be happy when something new is achieved, but one always has to think immediately about the next step. Susanne will realize that she must not make cuts in Steffi's development if Steffi is to be healed through education. In this process of development she has to realize that she has to make the series of goals acceptable to her child and take care that she will be able to reach them. For this the mother has to be very careful and sensitive in the support she gives, and she must take care to help only as much as is necessary, and to reduce the amount of help the next time.

If she still is unable to manage Steffi properly she should put this down to her own inexperience rather than to negative characteristics in the child, like laziness. We can well understand Susanne's fear. She does not yet believe enough in her own power, in her educational ability. She attributes laziness to Steffi, but "instinctively" evades the tasks which are not easy for herself, activating Steffi for walking, standing, and crawling and being responsible for these activities.

The case is as follows: In Steffi's brain function there is no connection between a rather distant goal and the possibility of being able to reach it using her legs. Her weakness is in the use of her legs. She does not realize that, to reach an aim, she could turn around on her front and creep there, or crawl, or walk somehow. These possibilities have to be made clear to her. For example, when she wants to have something and begins to creep to it, the mother can sit by her side and push her a bit on her bottom, or help at the thighs, so she can really reach her goal. When Steffi pushes a chair in front of her, her knees can be supported by her mother's hands so her still rather weak legs will not give way under her weight. It may also be necessary to lift her feet during walking.

Steffi now is at a stage that, whether or not she walks in a year's time (!) is dependent only upon her mother's encouragement. However, her mother must realize that this will not happen spontaneously. She must not and cannot wait for it, but has to overcome her fears and watch the situation closely, be aware of the present difficulties and also analyse them. In this way she will learn now to teach her child successfully.

A mother should always educate her child by using the causes of her present dissatisfaction as a pointer to the next necessary educational step. The mother of a motor-disordered child has to do this consciously, to help to overcome the child's difficulties. You have to do much more with such a child than with a healthy one. You have to be aware of the fact that each hour of cooperation speeds up the development by months.

Steffi's "laziness" is only temporary; this is characteristic for her present walking. It is lucky she can want something eagerly and persistently and can easily be motivated, for example by eating. At present Steffi should learn to use her legs. For this her mother should use goals that are important for Steffi (motivation) and can somehow be reached, like herself or a toy.

She uses her hands incessantly because she can use them successfully without too much effort. The same can and must be achieved for the legs. Only she will need some proper help, as you give Dina, if her legs cross when walking. She learns from the results she achieves with your help, and takes part in the activity more independently when it is repeated. That is why you have to help her less when she is walking sideways.

Maybe you can make these things clear to Susanne.

It is very difficult to understand the importance of intermediate steps in the gradual encouragement of learning.

If for example Dina has learned to stretch her arms above her head and to clap her hands there, but does not open her hands, you have to do that exercise specifically. For this she can lie on the plinth on her front or sit in front of a chair. Then you say a rhyme and let her pat with her palms on the bed or chair with her arms stretched, once with both hands simultaneously, once alternately. Seeing and hearing it will help her to open her hands. As soon as she has learned to clap her hands in front of her body she can practise clapping when sitting or lying (on her back), as well as above her head. Later on it will be enough for her to be told to open her hand. (Of course you have to take care that the thumbs are not under the fingers.)

Susanne will also learn step by step how to help her child, how to create the necessary conditions in a meaningful way and how to recognize and judge the results of her education. Perhaps she is afraid to destroy the happiness that arises from Steffi's development by looking at it too critically. But the opposite is true. Her contentment will combine with her growing self-confidence and her pride at being able to do everything through her own efforts. She will realize the immense importance of the mother's role in overcoming of the difficulties of a child with cerebral palsy, a role which is neglected and denied by so many.

You, Caroline, can see that quite clearly now. You gave us an example; as Dina got tired whilst sitting, and bent forward, your words were sufficient to make her sit straight again.

In an age in which scientific research is concentrated on space and atoms and so needs very complicated instruments, it seems nearly unbelievable that the scarcely perceptible help of a mother could influence a child's personality development so decisively. This human-biological fact can achieve something that neither medicine, nor surgery, nor technology can achieve - overcoming the difficulties of a motor-disordered child.

It is not surprising therefore that mothers find it so difficult to believe in their power.

Note on paralysis

Eva Galla underlined the above paragraph in her translation. We want to complete it.

Please remember that Dina, who sits straight when reminded by her mother, who uses her hands purposively, who has started walking, was diagnosed as paralysed in both arms and feet. These movements that Dina can make wilfully are, according to specialists, not possible in her case. Dina's severe, organic paralysis seemed actually uncorrectable some time ago.

Petö would never have accepted such an opinion. In his Institute the term "lame" was not used.

Because of this it is understandable that mothers have to be convinced of these possibilities and that Susanne needs your help and your encouragement to learn. But this is also the case for Dina's further development. For the next one or two years Dina and Steffi will need a group, which will at first only consist of the two of them, then of four or five children of about the same age and with similar problems. Then finally they will be able go to a regular kindergarten or school and their parents will at last forget the difficulties with which their child's life had begun. (The specialists will then doubt the former diagnosis and prognosis.)

So for the children's development the cooperation of mothers and fathers needs to increase. (That reminds me: How did the father to whom you wrote react?) In your case it is just a small group of children. But it is unavoidable that the number of such groups will grow when other interested parents hear about them.

In biology this sort of interaction is by no means rare. We put our trust in the mothers' cooperation, so the problem of cerebral palsy, which is so immense now, can one day be reduced considerably.

However, the resistance of specialists and institutions must not be underestimated. It should not be provoked but avoided as far as possible. For example, health insurance assumes that cerebral palsy is in most cases incurable. This is wrong - as we know - but it is the well-intentioned basis for funding resulting treatment costs. Maybe you should tell them, as the Hungarian papers reported (and perhaps also the German ones), that there was a demonstration in Great Britain on November 15th 1986 in front of the Houses of Parliament in London for the establishment of a "Petö Institute". Maybe you should also tell them that the Director of the Petö Institute in Budapest is a physician, but not her deputy and the main staff. They "only" have a diploma for conductors. However, their training is sufficient for the extraordinary success of an Institute that is known all over the world.

Physicians do not learn the Petö System as it is an educational one and educationalists do not learn it because it is a medical one. The conductors are trained at the Institute in Budapest and get a State-approved diploma. The Institute comes under the Ministry of Education and the Arts, not under the Ministry of Health...

I think a lecture in H. is generally possible, but there are some things that have to be thought about, for example whether it is good for the gradual development that has just started. This is a long process, pushed forward by Dina's and Steffi's progress. We think that at the moment the only thing that is promising is the "organic" cooperation of parents who are affected and other interested people. Every interference by an institution might hinder or slow down the development.

We would like to know what sort of an institution the "Diakonische Werke" is - we only know that it is an ecclesiastical one.

We do not know the women from Vienna who were there...

This is the end of the letter to Caroline. Now you can translate it. We hope that Caroline keeps these letters so she can read them again and again, especially the booklet, as old advice gets a new meaning in a new situation.

We want Caroline to copy these messages for Susanne.

Now you will understand better what we mean by "personality". Personality development starts in a group which for an infant consists only of himself and his mother. However, this group will soon get bigger, and so more complicated "intercerebral cooperation" with other people will develop. Personality development is created by the human-biological change in the individual's brain function which facilitates an increasing ability to cooperate with others.

One example of this is the way you support Caroline and Dina and how these two support Susanne and Steffi. This not only develops the children's personality, which is the most obvious change, but also that of the mothers and your own too. Each success is at the same time the basis for new challenges and thus for new successes for all members of the group. This gives all those who join in it the feeling of living a meaningful life.

Note by Eva Galla about the meaning of life
That is right! If it were not so I would not have succeeded in doing all that translating work. The feeling of doing something meaningful gave me the power to work for hours, until late at night! - Eva.

We must think about writing another booklet for the parents whose children are already on the way to overcoming their difficulties, children for which kindergarten activities have to be organised...

14 December 1986

From Caroline Seiffer:

A few days ago Susanne and Steffi were here again. We read your letter together and I advised her to write to you. She does not agree with some points and I cannot explain it to her. She thinks Steffi is lazy and that she can do everything at home, and she thinks too that Steffi should be able to do everything as she can understand everything and even says: "I want to walk." If it does not work then she says, for example: "Now start walking, go!"

But I have to say that Steffi has made good progress during the last few weeks and I praised her a lot. She can stand for a longer time and when supported at the arms she can go across the room with her chair.

Dina and Steffi were very glad to meet again and we are sorry that we live so far apart from each other. In January Dina and I will go to see Susanne. She has already built up a relatively big group, but that is easier in a big city, I suppose.

I am afraid I was not able to make any advances in that direction. There is no child of about the same age here with similar difficulties. Once a week we go to a playgroup of handicapped children, but I fear this is not of much use for Dina, as the other children are mentally handicapped and not motor-disordered, so there is not much cooperation there.

Now I want to report about the children. I took some photos.

This is the way Dina walks at her chair now. I only correct the legs from behind, which do not cross so much when wearing shoes from the Institute as without them. Perhaps you get the impression that she leans on the chair, but that is wrong.

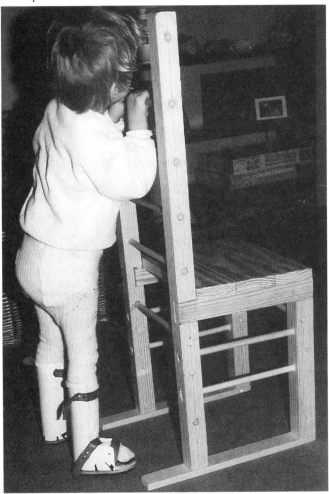

The ladder-back chair seems to be too heavy. The rungs should go down to the floor under the seat.

She often stands just holding with one hand, and when I support her knees a bit she can even stand without holding on.

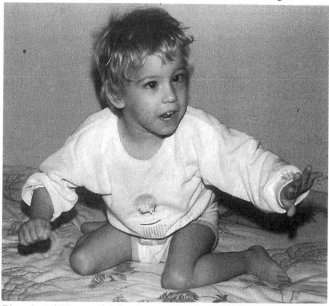

Dina adopted this way of sitting for some time, it was her first way of sitting alone. Because her legs were wide open in this position, she has now learned to sit cross-legged. She can now lift her arms when sitting and do "Pat-a-cake, pat-a-cake, baker's man", often with her mouth open. She does open her hands more often now.

You can see that we are doing something and are having a lot of fun and joy with the children.

Please allow us, dear reader, to repeat this sentence again: "You can see that we are doing something and are having a lot of fun and joy with the children."

Dina has now learned to point to things she wants to have. She can turn the pages in her picture book and wants me to read and sing a lot to her. Then she "talks" her "double dutch" and I look forward to the day she will really start talking.

138

This is new. The two chidren practise sitting alone, without help..

Both when playing. Dina frequently caressed Steffi and was glad that she was there.

This is the nice way Steffi can stand now. Susanne has changed the walking. Before she used to go behind Steffi and support her legs, but then Steffi's arms sagged. Now she supports the arms from the front and so the legs do not give way so easily. As she crosses her legs less often now, this works quite well. So we can help each other quite well.

At the moment I do not have any special questions. When I forget or have doubts about something I read your numerous letters and always find an answer there.

I did not hear from the father I wrote to...

140

27 December 1986

To Caroline Seiffer:

We were very glad about your letter and the photos, they were quite instructive and we see that our expectations for Dina's future are confirmed. We wait for your further reports about Dina's and Steffi's development and about how the group of mothers and children gets on...

31 December 1986

To Eva Galla:

We hope you got through the trouble of translating our long letter, but it was your own fault asking your question about "personality".

Now we just want to answer Caroline's letter.

This letter and the enclosed photos not only show Dina's and Steffi's development and the importance of a meeting between those two, but also the enormous development Caroline is going through. This can be seen in her close observation of the children's problems and her descriptions of how to find a solution, in how important it is for her to pass her knowledge on to Susanne and her assured grasp of the right educational solution. One good example of her achievements is the following; she showed Susanne how to teach her daughter to walk using the chair, that is by Steffi gripping a rung of the chair on which the mother sits and pushes herself backwards. This way the child can move towards her mother, and she is motivated to walk. This will stop Steffi's "laziness".

It can also be seen from picture 5 that Steffi does not grip very well yet. She only hooks her fingers to the rung instead of gripping with her entire hand. So Steffi must be taught to grip with her whole hand. You need to make sure that her fingers lie next to each other, opposite to the thumb. In this way her hand will close. The wrist should be bent dorsally, that is towards the back of the hand. Her mother should help her for some time, then she should show it to her and accompany the action with a description, until it will be enough to remind Steffi if she forgets it. She will do it immediately then.

The picture also shows Steffi's tendency to lean backwards, or, to be more concrete, that her soles do not lie flat on the floor, there is an obtuse angle between foot and leg. This strengthens the tendency to lean backwards. This is made worse by her mother's support from behind. The tendency to lean backwards makes Steffi unsteady when walking or standing and thus timid. This might be a reason why Steffi avoids walking (being "lazy"). Because of this it would be good for her to get the same boots that Dina has. The main point of these boots is that they maintain the correct angle between foot and leg. They not only prevent standing on the toes, but also crossing of the legs and the tendency to lean back.

But she has to sustain the correct position of the feet in all situations (when sitting, lying, standing), and always when playing. When she is able to reach and maintain the desired position she must be told so and praised. She will learn that she has achieved what her mother expected from her, from her mother's contentment, and not automatically.

At first mothers have to learn to recognize those aspects of their child's problem that are very important but which, because of their apparent insignificance, can only be consciously recognized with difficulty. If they do not acquire this ability they will not be able to recognize its value nor teach their children anything. In the book "*Conductive Education*" by Hári/Akos this faculty is called "conductive (operative) observation". Caroline already possesses this skill and when trying to teach this to Susanne she must remember that this takes much time and patience.

Susanne did not realize what happened when Steffi said: "I want to walk", but then did not start walking. Perhaps we confused her by saying "she does not realize", although we put it in inverted commas. Obviously Steffi wanted (!) to walk, but was not yet able to do so. This does not mean that she is lazy. The intention and its execution are not yet connected in her brain.

142

The muscles of the leg do not get the necessary "instructions", although there is the wish to walk. (Specialists would say her legs are not yet integrated in her "body image", at least not entirely.)

Both children should learn to get up from their front to their knees by gripping one rung of the chair, and then pulling themselves up to a squatting position and finally standing up by gripping the next higher rungs with both hands alternately. (Of course without boots.) They should do the same the other way round, that is from a standing position down to a squatting one, then onto the knees and down onto their front. Dina does not use both hands equally, so Caroline should try to bring the unused hand more into use.

As far as learning to talk is concerned, Caroline has to take care that Dina learns the apparently peripheral movements, like licking the lips, blowing, sucking, and swallowing her saliva, as these voluntary movements of the mouth and tongue are essential for learning the coordinated movements of talking. She is near speaking in an understandable way, but this can be speeded up by these measures. In this, too, it is important to show her the desired activities and to articulate them.

24 January 1987

From Caroline Seiffer:

Thanks a lot for your Christmas greetings and the letter to Eva. There are always many important instructions and I often take out your letters and re-read them.

Originally I wanted to go and see Susanne at the beginning of January, but the snow thwarted our plans. One could no longer go by car and the trains had delays of several hours... So we had to postpone our visit and will most probably go at the beginning of February. Nevertheless I want to write to you and I hope that Susanne has done the same in the meantime. Steffi had a bad cold that seems to have set her back quite a bit, but Susanne said that she already knows that.

Note on the temporary deterioration because of an illness

Any illness will worsen the general function of the brain. Febrile illnesses with children often influence the personality in a temporarily unfavourable way. In severe cases generalised convulsions can occur, even if the child is not epileptic. In less severe cases the child's activity diminishes or stops, and he becomes weary.

Motor-disturbed children may temporarily lose faculties they had acquired beforehand, and symptoms that had been overcome can recur.

One has to know that. But one should also know that after the illness the state reached previously will be reestablished. Nevertheless one should be careful after an illness and not tire the child, in other words have breaks or exercise less.

Susanne wants to come to Budapest again in April or May, so I suppose we will come together. I will write to Frau Dr Hári to ask if we can come. Although I think I manage things quite well, a "refresher course" will do us both good.

During recent weeks Dina has experienced an enormous change. She has discovered herself and her own power. Unlike my two other children she has always been obstinate, but now she gets her own way to such an extent that I am sometimes at a complete loss, yet sometimes too I am enthusiastic because now she sets the goals. She motivates herself, discovers things, points at them and shows with little sounds that she wants to have them. Then I say: "Well, come on, let's go and get it." Then she first has to do all the things that are necessary for getting up (with my help, of course), that is rising from lying on her front to the knees, to a squatting position and then up. As soon as she stands, she actually runs, with rapid steps, that are often too wide, towards the goal. I hold her at the arms from the front and correct the position of her legs. At the moment she does not want to walk with the chair. Usually she fights against this so strongly that I leave it alone. I can easily motivate her to stand, for example to watch the birds eating. Standing there she often needs no more than slight support at the hips.

In the meantime I got an answer from the father to whom I had written in response to his request in the periodical. He wrote that he was not very successful with gymnastics and that he had stopped doing them and worked according to Petö without knowing it. In the last few months he had adapted himself to his child and tried to build on the first signs of change through motivation and patience. We will go on corresponding.

Eva asked me to give you her kind regards, she will be too busy to write for the next few weeks and months. Eva is going to be self-employed, she will open her own music school. For this she had to rent a house and furnish it. She will soon move...

30 January 1987

From Susanne Gross:

Now it is high time you heard something from us. Thanks a lot for your letters, again and again they have shown us things that help us further.

Between Christmas and New Year Steffi, for the first time in her life, had a fever which reached as high as 102.9F. Everything was over after three days but then two weeks ago we all had a cold and she had a high temperature again. She was really weary, for two days her temperature was back to normal, but then it rose again.

This quite exhausted her. She could sit on a stool easily with the help of a ladder-back chair at her side. She even let go of the rungs sometimes, but now she is afraid again. I have to motivate her a great deal and stabilise her at the knee or shoulder. Meanwhile a few days have passed since her illness and she is now recovering.

In her room she can easily move forward by crawling.

Note on crawling

Here crawling means creeping on the tummy. The child moves using his arms, but his legs remain stretched and are not used. It is not good to let a child who is already starting to walk, but has difficulties with his legs crawl. Steffi's main problem is that she is unable to integrate her legs into her body image, in other words she cannot move them in a coordinated way. As a game it will not do much harm for a short period of time, although it is a waste of time as it does not contribute to personality development. The mother, who certainly has enough work already, could use this time better for games that develop her child's personality.

We want to mention something else. With a child who has a tendency to stand on his toes, positions in which the foot is not at a right angle to the leg should be avoided. This applies to crawling as well as, for example, to sitting cross-legged.

From time to time she also moves her legs on her own, but most of the time I help her and say: "I bend my right (left) leg up".

Sometimes Steffi can even kneel on all fours, for example when we play "dog", and then she starts bobbing up and down.

When crawling she often holds her hand on its back. I show and tell her that the hands must lay flat on the palm, then she can do it on her own. Steffi even says now that she wants to walk. I take her from the front, stretch her arms, but still have to stabilise her firmly. Then she will sing a song and we go wherever she wants to. I am afraid we need a second person that could hold her legs from behind as she often crosses them or walks on her toes. When she stands at the ladder-back chair and I hold her legs, she does not stretch her arms, but bends them.

Note on the use of certain aids

In this situation it would be advisable to wear "Petö boots" to add to the mother's support and prevent crossing the legs and tip-toeing. Then the mother could use her hands to support stretching of the arms. However, if the child had an elbow splint to support the outstretched arms, he could move the chair forward and the mother could support the legs (cf. photos in Hári/Ákos: Conductive Education).

However, both aids are only to be used temporarily for supporting learning in the actual phase of walking. At another time the child should learn to put his heels down and to stretch his arms. In this way the aids will gradually become superfluous.

Next weekend Caroline Seiffer is coming to see us. We had to postpone our meeting once because of the bad winter. She said on the phone that we could have Dina's shoes for some time, as Dina walks without them more often. Maybe I could ask an orthopaedic shoemaker here whether he could make such shoes as well.

Steffi's heels are on the floor when she stands, for example, in front of the bird's cage. She likes to do that and then her knees are stretched as well.

This is because of the lifting of the head, as well as the energetic effect of her motivation which also reduces muscle spasm.

At the moment we are training her to grip the rungs correctly. We can do this when she sits on her potty or the stool and her ladder-back chair is in front of her.

Steffi now wants to eat on her own, to spread butter on bread, to eat with a spoon or a fork... I am not allowed to help her.

She talks a lot now and nearly sings songs on her own. I think she is learning to talk well from the healthy child of my friend, who is about the same age as Steffi and whom we meet often. In our neighbourhood there is a four-year-old boy with similar difficulties to Steffi who has been able to walk a few metres for four weeks. The mother is very interested in the Petö method and we are together a lot...

Now we have the possibility of sending our two children to a normal kindergarten. It is a group for two hours each afternoon, consisting of five children and our two. I want to be there at first, to involve the nursery nurses in the method. The whole thing is a trial to begin with.

...I wonder whether Dina will like it here and whether she will recognize Steffi. I can take Steffi anywhere, she has no difficulties in adapting herself as long as I am with her...

Today I realized that Steffi has recently crossed her legs more than usual. Is it possible that this is the effect of sitting cross-legged? Steffi can sit quite well with her legs crossed, so I used this position quite often.

28 February 1987

To Caroline Seiffer:

We were very happy about your last letter and are looking forward to the next one.

Dina is developing wonderfully well. You are very good at educating her.

I enclose a copy of my letter to Susanne for your information. We have to make new plans now to develop present achievements further. I have to tell you that we are worried about how groups for children will work out, as this demands another sort of education from the mothers. The written material we want to send to you may help a little, anyway, but correspondence is a clumsy form of communication.

28 February 1987

To Susanne Gross:

...You are a close observer of your child and have already achieved good results.

1. Steffi's tendency to cross her legs when walking is neither surprising nor alarming. I suppose you are right with your idea that sitting frequently with her legs crossed has contributed quite a lot to it. It would be better for Steffi to sit on a stool,

then you have to take care that the soles of her feet are on the floor. When sitting cross-legged, the feet are stretched, which has to be avoided. This does not mean however that it cannot be allowed for some short time. By the way, no posture should be maintained too long, this is especially true for sitting cross-legged.

It is most important to teach Steffi not to cross her legs. She can learn this first when sitting or lying. Teach her to open ("I move my legs apart") and close her legs ("I put my legs together").

You could make a game. Take two dolls and put them on her feet, which she moves apart and closes again. (The dolls can be made of paper and be fastened with a rubber band.) There are many such games. This will make clear to Steffi what she is supposed to do. She will then correct the position of her legs as well when walking, if you tell her that her legs are not standing correctly. At first you can help Steffi by standing in front of her, taking her hands in yours and putting one foot between hers, so they cannot cross.

2. At the moment we do not think Steffi should go to a non-conductive regular kindergarten. She is now at an intermediate stage when she will acquire the adaptibility which is necessary for cooperation with healthy children in the kindergarten. A child's education and the play that is necessary for overcoming her difficulties should be organized by the mother at this stage. The appropriate group consists now of sisters and brothers, or other children with similar problems. We are preparing some written instructions for the mothers at the moment.

9 March 1987

From Caroline Seiffer:

... Three weeks ago we went to see Susanne. The journey was very exhausting and the trains were delayed by several hours. After that Dina and I had a very bad cold, actually we only recovered a few days ago. Susanne and Steffi will soon come to see us again.

There is not much I can say about our visit as we did not have enough time to talk about things in detail. Besides, Frau Baumann and her son were there as well. But it is always a good thing to meet again and there is a lot to talk about.

I already mentioned in my last letter that we want to come to Budapest in May. I wrote to Frau Dr Hári in January, but have not got an answer yet. Susanne wants very much to take part in the second course and I think it will be good for Dina and me as well. We intend to fly on the 3rd and start at the Institute on the 4th.

There is not much important news about Dina. The illness set her back quite a bit, but she recovered rapidly. I enjoy working with her very much as now I see that she can understand everything. This discovery was a very important one for me. Now I accept Dina more than I did before and my fears are disappearing. It is a wonderful experience to feel her reaction. Her fits of anger are beginning to disappear; I always countered them by telling Dina: "Now we both go where you want to go and you show me what you want". Like this we can both achieve our goals.

At the moment I do not have any special questions.

I am curious about what the material you are going to send will be like.

Eva has moved...Now she has even less time as she is self-employed and every pupil is important. She sends you her kindest regards.

By the way, our health insurance paid the costs of the Institute and half those of the flight...

21 March 1987

To Caroline Seiffer:

...It is a pity your visit to Susanne and Steffi did not go very well because of the bad weather.

Meanwhile you will certainly have got the answer from the Petö Institute. We are looking forward to seeing you and Dina, Susanne and Steffi on May 3rd. If your answer from the Institute was a negative one, please tell me about it, I will then try to change it, although things like this have become difficult, as there are so many foreign children at the Institute. This endangers the care of Hungarian children.

There are many children from Britain, as there is an arrangement with the University of Birmingham to establish a Petö Institute in Great Britain. This will be the second Petö Institute in a foreign country. The first is in Japan.

The costs of treatment have been increased considerably and it is good that you get them refunded by your health insurance. What I cannot understand is why you only got half the cost of the flight.

I think it can be safely assumed that, sooner or later, the FRG will wake up and establish a Petö Institute as well. It was very wise of you not to wait for that and look for your own solutions.

Note on the foundation of Petö Institutes

If one starts thinking about the number of people with motor disorders, which I suppose is about the same everywhere, in the FRG perhaps as high as 50,000, it becomes clear that one single Petö Institute in a country will not solve the problem.

The problem is not only the cost of founding several institutes, but also the training of an appropriate number of specialists (conductors). The problems seem to be immense.

This remark is only intended to guide sensible questioning.

The things you wrote about your numerous activities, about how Dina can now understand everything and about her wonderful cooperation with you, can be taken as a very good sign for Dina's further development. (The mental and physical development of children with cerebral palsy do influence each other positively and should therefore be equally encouraged.)

When Dina reaches school age her personality may then be on the same level as that of other children of the same age. So she will be able to fulfil the demands of a regular school! This prognosis is realistic, but depends on certain conditions. We have described these in the enclosed paper (see below).

You will see that overcoming the difficulties of cerebral palsy depends on changing the child's personality, on her "metamorphosis". During the first three years of life the mother initiates this change, as it is she who has the decisive influence on her child's development at that age. The mother will later lose this "monopoly". You know from your own experiences that the mother achieves the apparently "wonderful" disappearance of symptoms by strengthening and guiding the child's motivation.

Like this the mother succeeds in changing her child's personality, which enables the child to cooperate with her more and more. Any child is motivated to cooperate with his mother, and the mother's influence depends on this fact. She can learn to increase the child's motivation and thus her independence in a way which not only satisfies her needs but also overcomes the symptoms of her motor disturbance. (Striving for independence is motivation as well, as can be seen when a child protests against superfluous help: "Leave me, I'll do it on my own!")

At the age when children go to kindergarten there is a new motivation, their intense interest in other children and the wish to come into contact with them. This new motivation is very important for further personality development. Unlike before, when the mother learned to work successfully with her child, this is a totally new task for her.

In the enclosed paper we comment only briefly on the general meaning of this new motivation but we hope we can make clear that the previous mother-child relationship will not suffice any more. In future, three or four mothers with similar problems and their children of about the same age should meet regularly and do things together. However, the mothers must not depend on their children's spontaneous initiatives, but should use the necessary "channelling" help, as described. This will be important for Dina too in the near future. At first it will be enough to meet two or three times a week for one or two hours, later on it will have to be more.

After an initial period the presence of all mothers together will be superfluous, so they can be present alternately. The number of children can be increased according to changes in the children's situation. This is valid for the next two or three years. In the paper we will talk about this in greater detail. Some problems seem to be difficult to solve at first sight, but this impression is a wrong one.

One has to be aware of the fact that at least one out of five hundred newborn babies is motor-disordered. So there should be three or four mothers living near you or Susanne whose 2- or 3-year-old children are not treated to their mother's satisfaction. It is possible that the physicians who used to be so sceptical are pleased about the enormous change in your children and will give you addresses of other mothers. But the next steps cannot be done by the mothers alone. Perhaps you or Susanne could establish a society with and for the mothers. These "societies of metamorphosis" are meant to give the children with motor disturbances the support they need for their personality development and so for becoming healthy.

We want to point out some goals that might be strived for by these societies.

The mothers of children with motor disorders or of children who are suspected to be affected (for example when born prematurely) should be given our booklet. There should be advice centres where the mothers are supported and the necessary equipment is bought (e.g. a plinth, some ladder-back chairs, boots, mugs with two handles and so on).

These societies can also help to organize the above mentioned children's groups and put rooms and equipment at their disposal. Capable conductors should be trained and employed. Specialists, for example educationalists, can acquire the knowledge which is specifically needed. There might even be some mothers who are able and interested in becoming conductors in a kindergarten.

The German societies should contact the Hungarian Institute and organize stays for children who need to be at the Institute for a longer time, because the Petö System was begun too late with them.

One could even think about cooperation with the Hungarian Petö Institute to establish a German one, as happened in Japan and as is happening now in Great Britain. Lectures and courses should be organized for specialists who are interested in the method.

The local societies will most probably grow, new ones will be established and these can contact each other. This way more and more finance can be raised from various sources, such as the state, communities, the churches and private sponsors, and there can be people working in honorary positions...

The societies should always be led by interested parents and be free from egotistic and bureaucratic tendencies.

When we thought about these problems, we agreed to the following. To be able to realize this plan my wife and I will have to come to the FRG for two or three years. We must not let Dina and Steffi down after their immense successes. We feel responsible for the further development of these children. I know the Petö Institute in Budapest very well. Many members of the senior staff were my students when I gave lectures about Conductive Education there. I wrote the book *Conductive Education*, which was published in 1971, on the request of Frau Dr Hári, the co-author. I have been working independently from the Institute for many years. My wife and I were able to explain the metamorphosis of personality through "anthropogenic cooperation" because of our research about general brain function. So we can give a theoretical basis for the Petö System. Our youngest daughter is a qualified conductor in the Petö Institute and has a lot of experience.

As Susanne is facing the same problems as you do, we sent her a copy of this letter and the enclosed material.

Please give our regards to Eva. As she is so busy with her school we do not want to trouble her with the translation.

A letter to mothers whose children have developed as a result of Conductive Education and are now reaching kindergarten age.

What does "kindergarten age" mean?

"Kindergarten age" does not mean a particular number of years but a phase of the child's personality development. Before this time only the mother (or a person to whom the child is closely related) can start and sustain the changes which allow the child's difficulties to be overcome. An apathetic child becomes an active and lively one with goals and a mind of his own. In this metamorphosis the child also learns to overcome the symptoms of cerebral palsy, with his mother's help.

Success is only possible with the mother's guidance. The mother must learn to assess the child's motivations and to work out how to help him reach his goals. This will teach the child to be increasingly and extensively independent.

The precondition for this is the child's own motivation to cooperate with his mother.

If the mother starts to treat her child during the first months of life, the infant will soon lose the symptoms of cerebral palsy, perhaps in the course of a few months. If the mother does not start using the Petö System before the first or second year, a complete revovery will take longer. During the first few years of life success comes from the anthropogenic cooperation between mother and child, from the mother's influence on the development of the child's personality.

When the child reaches kindergarten age, the mother faces a new and unexpected motivation. She has been successful up until then because she recognized, satisfied and therefore channelled the child's motivation. Her experiences are restricted to that sort of motivation. But from about the third year the child will show great interest in other children of the same age. Normally the mother encourages that spontaneously by taking her child to a playground or a kindergarten.

Reaching kindergarten age

The concept of a kindergarten developed out of the experience that children are interested in each other, want to be together and form groups. Ad hoc groups of children sometimes lead to unexpected results, with which the parents are quite rightly not satisfied. The educator's task is to channel the children's motivations, to organize their interactions and to integrate them into the group and thus into society. This includes the imparting of capabilities, skills and knowledge.

Children who cannot be integrated in a group because they either constantly draw back or get aggressive and disturb the others, will be excluded from the kindergarten because they are not mature enough.

Children whose life began with a motor disturbance, but whose symptoms could be entirely or partly eliminated with their mother's help, will probably experience problems in a regular kindergarten: they might be seen as "easily tiring", "clumsy", "slow", "not able to keep up with the others", "withdrawn" or "aggressive", "not able to play in a group" and so on. The mother becomes dissatisfied with the child's development at home, can see that past achievements are being lost, realizes that kindergarten does her child harm, and so keeps him at home again.

She already knows that she can recognize and guide her child's motivation and so encourage his personality development and diminish the symptoms of the damage.

What can be done in such a situation?

The special conductive, transitional kindergarten

Work in the kindergarten has two goals: one is apparent, the other is less obvious and pursued through various activities. Textbooks of kindergarten education list knowledge, skills and capabilities which the educator should impart, and which aim at increased orientational ability and the encouragement of practical skills. The children almost automatically learn to adapt themselves to each other and to cooperate; these are faculties which are important for personality development, a fact that educationalists do not recognize sufficiently often.

A child who is freed nearly or entirely from motor disorder symptoms at an age when he should go to a kindergarten has been guided by his mother in this learning process. She has succeeded because she had reinforced the child's ability to cooperate with her.

The child's motivation to cooperate with his mother is now joined by another motivation; that of wanting to cooperate with a group of children of the same age. Normally children learn through apparently spontaneous, anthropogenic cooperation with each other. But this can be channelled by their educators.

If however the children have various difficulties caused by their motor disorders, conductors are needed to structure this cooperation and to reduce the difficulties gradually.

One can imagine such a conductive kindergarten for those children who have overcome most of their difficulties because their mothers have treated them using the Petö System. These small children come with their mothers, who bring their knowledge and experiences which they gained by working with their own children, while the educator brings her ability to organize kindergarten activities.

At first such a group will only consist of three or four children. As soon as they get used to each other the number of children can be increased gradually, but never by more than one child at a time.

The equipment is not out of the ordinary. Only simple things are needed, things which the mothers already know and which are very useful, for example light, mobile and versatile plinths, ladder-back chairs, stools, poles, ropes, rings, stairs and inclined slopes for active games, crayons of different thicknesses, paints, paper, modelling clay and so on.

However the equipment is not the most essential aspect of these kindergartens. It is also wrong to think that only children with the same level of achievement can be brought together.

Children with motor disorders are never the same, neither in the problems they have, nor in the solutions of those problems. This is not a disadvantage, but an advantage for the group, as each child can have his own area where he is successful and can see that other children have the same difficulties in other areas. So there are always some members of the group who can serve as good examples for others and who will show them the right way of doing things.

It is essential that the children's level of achievement is raised through common games and activities, where every child gets just as much help as he needs. Up until now each mother helped her child directly and appropriately. Now the mothers have to learn how to support their children's correct cooperation, indirectly. The children will learn just as before by getting gradually less help and by increasing their ability to cooperate with other children.

To learn this new form of promoting cooperation the mothers will need the help of a trained conductor.

This form of conductive kindergarten arose from the needs of mothers who had to face the problems caused by their children's development. But you cannot always wait for a trained conductor. Some educators could take up this challenge and with appropriate instructions - like the mothers - could work together with mothers who have already proved that they can help their children through Conductive Education. They should read both Hári and Akos: *Conductive Education* and Akos and Akos: *Dina*; they should also learn how to analyze the mothers's information about their children and how to utilize it in common games.

At first the most important components are the mothers' special knowledge and experience of their children's needs, the knowledge of educationalists, and written and oral instruction in Conductive Education.

The children will spend more and more time in this kindergarten, as their ability to meet their own demands increases, and so will develop further.

Soon it will not be necessary for all mothers to be present. At first they should come in turn, then their presence will not be needed at all.

Finally the children can be integrated into a regular kindergarten.

Some mothers, whose children are finally integrated into a regular kindergarten without problems, might want to work in a conductive kindergarten and become trained conductors. Other mothers help in advice centres for other families with motor-disordered infants. (There will be an increasing need for this.)

31 March 1987

To Caroline Seiffer:

...I talked with Dr Hári after your phone-call. She told me that both of you have already been accepted.

4 April 1987

From Susanne Gross:

... A week ago Steffi and I went to see Caroline and Dina again. We even stayed a day longer. Dina got used to us very well.

At the moment we call each other every second day, as I am curious whether we will all meet again in May.

I want to thank you very much for your letter. Last Friday Frau Baumann got her letter and I copied it at once...

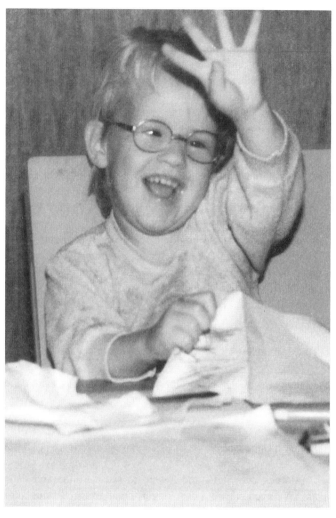
Steffi when drawing

Steffi is very well now. She talks the whole day long and loves to play role games. She is the mother and I am the child.

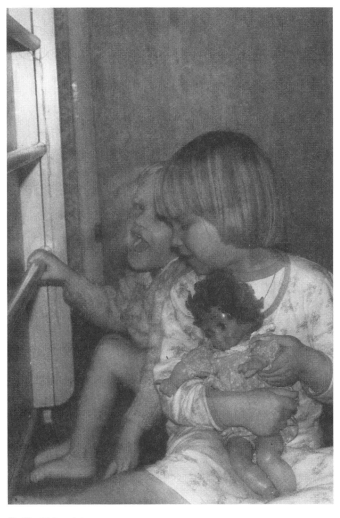
Steffi with her sister

Recently she asked me whether I was thirsty and I said yes. Then she said: "Then you must have a drink at my breast" and pulled up her vest and pullover. She was just sitting on her potty.

Some weeks ago we got a plinth, on which she likes to sleep. But she does not like to lie on it when the blankets are off; she has not done this in the Institute before either.

I enclose a picture of Steffi. When I look at it closely I can see that her feet are not flat on the floor and her hand does not grip correctly...

Note on the mother's observation

One can see very well from Frau Gross' remarks about the picture that she has learned to observe her daughter.

When she was here the last time we showed her that Steffi was facing the wall, her back turned to the room. So she was "excluded" from the world and not motivated enough; that is why she did not sit correctly. The mother understood at once what we meant, it was an "aha!" experience for her.

7 April 1987

From Caroline Seiffer:

Today I got your acceptance, after Eva had already told me the good news on the phone. Thank you very much for your trouble. I have not heard anything from the Institute yet, although I have written twice. Now it has become a bit more difficult to get a cheap Lufthansa flight. One has to book 8 weeks in advance to get a 40% reduction. It also takes some time to get the visa. But Susanne and I have arranged everything, so I think we will come on May 3rd...

I have not got your letter yet, but Susanne sent me a copy of hers. I read it quickly, but it is so interesting that I will re-read it tonight in peace and quiet.

I am trying to get a children's group together; I will tell you about this soon.

Perhaps you got a letter from a Frau Haug in the meantime. She rang me up and told me that she had got my address from the University of Birmingham, together with your booklet. She is a teacher of physically and mentally handicapped children and is very interested in the Petö method. She has already been in Birmingham and knows a lot. Up until now she only knew the method, but had not heard about any concrete success here. So it was very important for her to hear that Dina is an example of it and will be so in future, as I truly believe.

Frau Haug told me about a German professor who had been in Budapest twice; she seems to be trying to present the method scientifically here. I will soon find out more about it.

Last week Susanne and Steffi were here for four days. It was very good for us and we were both glad to be able to find new advances made by our children. Meanwhile Steffi is able to stand for a very long time and also makes good progress in sitting and supporting herself. Dina is still practising her talking, she utters unconnected syllables like: "Agagigu" and the like. When I repeat the names a few times and when she looks at me and is interested she can say: "Han-ne, El-sie".

We will soon be able to talk about everything else.

18 May 1987

The following letter comprises all the experiences, impressions and insights we could gain during the stay of the two mothers and their children.

To Caroline Seiffer:

In this letter we want to describe Dina's present situation in a more detailed way than we did before.

Dina loves to walk. However, compared with her former way of walking it has changed unfavourably. She walks too fast, she nearly runs if you hold her body and balance for her, instead of letting her do it on her own. She walks with her trunk bent forward, her arms hanging inactively at her sides. If you let her go, she would fall on her face. What can one conclude from this?

Steffi has learned to sit and can move her hands freely. She is wearing "corrective boots" made of a simple (non-orthopaedic) wooden sole with a plastic leg and leather straps.

Dina's activity shows itself in her motivation to walk. It is very good to encourage her in this. So far you have reached a stage when her legs only cross occasionally when walking and - most important - she corrects this when you tell her to. Of course you should lead Dina further in this direction and practise opening of the legs when sitting and lying; you should also go on practising walking sideways, always intergrated in games of course. This way you will first succeed in teaching Dina to correct a wrong position of the legs when you tell her to, and later not to cross her legs at all.

She is now walking too fast because her centre of gravity is too far forward. To prevent falling there is a compensating movement. The wide steps can be explained in the same way. This compensating movement should be accompanied by characteristic movements of the arms, but these are lacking. It can be inferred from this that the arms are excluded from the coordination of the movements of the whole body in this position, that is from the "body image". So the main emphasis of Dina's education will be the integration of arms and hands (in various positions) into the body image. She will not learn to walk independently if she cannot solve this task.

Note on the "body image"

"Body image" is the expression of the general brain function, which coordinates all actual movements belonging to one activity, that is it combines the partial patterns into one whole pattern. Various muscles contract and relax according to a temporal regulation. The single partial patterns work unconsciously and cannot be wilfully influenced. The activities however can be made conscious. The more certain partial patterns combine into an entity, the less help is needed for their performance and the more their connection is confirmed. In her teaching the mother builds up the pattern in the child's brain step by step. By helping her child to solve his problems she "represents" a succession of single steps as a pattern in the child's brain.

The movements of all parts of the body are integrated in this whole pattern. One can often read or hear that it is determined by certain traits in the nervous system. This is wrong.

The same is true for each learning process: building the pattern takes more time than converting what has been learned. At first this convertion is a slow process. It takes a long time for an activity actually to start and then for the goal to be reached. One always has to keep this in mind when educating a motor-disordered child. A child must be given enough time and the necessary minimal support to be able to perform an activity independently. The mother should never do something which the child could do on his own - even if then it only happens slowly, for example eating or drinking.

How can a little girl be taught to integrate her arms and hands into her body image?

You have thought about such tasks several times; there are tasks for which Dina already uses her hands. So she has already learnt to use her hands in certain situations, but that does not work always, quite the contrary. Sometimes you get the impression that she had forgotten her hands, for example when she is thirsty and there is a glass of juice in front of her but she does not lift her arm to reach for it. Then when you give her something to drink, she drinks a lot. So the motivation is there but Dina does not become active. In this case it would be wrong just to give her something to drink. You should try to trigger off her activity by telling her to take the glass. When she tries to do so you give her the support she needs by putting your hands on hers and strengthening her grip, taking care that the glass does not fall over, and so on.

Treat Dina like someone who often forgets that she has got hands and must be reminded.

The satisfaction of Dina's needs and wishes should be combined with the active use of her hands. At first I am sure this will take a lot of time. But you should not force her.

She will of course need special help, for example, the two-handled mug, so she can easily grip and lift it. When she lifts it, you say: "I lift the mug". But you already know this. Activate the use of her hands as often as possible, for example when playing, eating, drinking, washing and dressing. If Dina expects you to do something for her which she could do on her own or could at least help you with, you must refuse to give this superfluous support and tell her: "You can do that on your own". Of course really necessary help, especially when she is ill, must never be refused. You should use each opportunity to reduce the help necessary, to encourage independence.

It is important now to keep Dina's hands busy as often as possible, the arms should not hang down passively either. This is another reason why she should walk while holding your forefingers or pushing a light (!) chair. (Perhaps it would be better if Dina gripped your thumbs so you can support her hands better.)

Dina has to get a feeling of security when walking. For this she needs to learn to maintain her balance and to save herself when falling. The following games might be helpful:

Dina stands behind a ladder-back chair and grips alternately the next lower rung until she is in a squatting position. Then she goes back the other way, thus standing up again. (This has to happen without the boots as they are too stiff and would prevent squatting. They are only used when the ankles are supposed to remain fixed.)

When we say "grip" we mean a more complex movement, that is the stretching of the arm to reach something, the gripping itself, the holding and handling of things (manipulating). There should always be some toys near her which she likes to hold and handle. At first she has to be made aware of them, as she will not see them, because the hands do not yet belong to her body image.

Besides manipulating things, Dina should learn to climb onto things. She should push herself down from the plinth with her hands, turn round and so on. She should walk between two rows of chairs and support herself alternately with her right and her left hand. This will teach her both walking and gripping. She should also walk between two poles which she can hold onto and stop after each step and lift first her right and then her left arm. (A possible motivation would be to wave to her sister.)

She will learn to let go with one hand more easily when walking, if you give her a rubber ring to hold.

There are various manipulating games in sitting and lying positions as well. Dina will take part in these games actively and use her hands alternately. The things she learns when playing, she will use in everyday activities, for example by helping you when eating, dressing or brushing her teeth.

To enable her to help with dressing, you have to put the clothes so she can easily reach them. For example pull the socks over her toes so she only has to pull them up; you can do the same with her trousers. Always tell her what she is doing. Praise Dina when she helps you actively; this is the only way for her to understand when she has done something correctly.

We want to emphasize again that Dina will only learn walking when she has learned to use both her hands for playing and helping you. This is the only way to teach her to use her arms and hands for balancing and to protect her when falling. To learn to walk it is not enough to use the legs in a coordinated way, arms and hands also have to be integrated into the body image.

This is also a condition for Dina's intellectual development. Words cannot be learned without concrete experiences. The mother's linguistic explanation belongs to these concrete experiences. You have to realize when Dina wants to go somewhere, what her goal is and put it in words. When the goal is reached you have to tell her that as well. This will make her aware that she has goals and what they are. Dina should have as many tactile experiences as possible on her way to her goal; she should feel, grasp and manipulate. The things she touches should be named, along with their colour, shape, and whether they are warm or cold. You also have to tell her the direction of an activity, whether she grasps, lifts up or puts down something. Tell her when she uses her left leg or arm and when she uses the right. This will help her perception, which is frequently disturbed in motor-disordered children.

All goals of education are complex. When Dina learns to walk with a chair, for example, she learns at the same time to stretch her arms. This is part of learning those movements of the arms which will protect her when falling. These movements are built into the process of learning to walk and encourage the feeling of security, which is a basic condition for walking.

Finally I want to say something about speech. The most important task for learning to speak actively is correct chewing. Because of this Dina should not have soft food which can be mashed between tongue and palate, but rather solid food. Give her hard things to gnaw at from time to time, like crusts and hard fruits, and crisp, crunchy things which can be crushed easily and which make a loud noise when being chewed.

This will make lips, tongue and jaws more mobile which is an important condition for articulation.

It is important to talk in the first person because in this way Dina will learn to express what she thinks, wants and does. (All people think in the first person about themselves.) At first the mother talks in the child's place, then the child joins her, first loudly, later only in thought. This way movements become conscious activities and serve to realize intentions. In this way the child learns to see and express the relation between her goals and the activities which lead to them. The practical activities will help to integrate hands and arms into the body image and also teach Dina to think about the use of her hands. (It often happens that motor-disturbed children, or adults with one paralyzed arm show people with just one arm in drawings because the other arm does not exist in their consciousness.)

The complex movements which are necessary for learning an activity or manipulation happen rather slowly. So the child needs not only a lot of patience to reach her goal, but also special, indirect support. One way to fill the time between the expression of the goal and its attainment, is, to count to five rhythmically. Small children can repeat the goal rhythmically, for example: "up, up, up, up,...." This is called "rhythmic intention" in Conductive Education, one of the many little tricks which are very important in the Petö System.

This time we will not write to Susanne, she will read this letter and certainly will be able to use a lot of it.

It was a pleasant surprise for us to hear that Steffi and Wolfgang (Frau Baumann's son) have educators that are able and ready to cooperate. If they could read our material and talk about it with the mothers, it would be very good for the continuation of the mother's education. We have a very positive opinion of these educators.

We are sorry to say that this never happened.

Dina - A Summary
Practising the Petö System makes it possible to overcome cerebral palsy.

Note on the available material
Caroline Seiffer intended to write a report about her experiences to help other mothers. We wanted to help her with the available material and gave it to her and Susanne Gross when they were in Budapest.
It is a summary of the whole correspondence.

Cerebral Palsy not only affects the child but also his family and society. According to Schlack there are 2-3 children with cerebral palsy in every 1000 births; the "Bundesverband für spastisch Gelähmte und andere Körperbehinderte" (Association for People with Spastic Palsy and other Physical Handicaps) talks about 3-4 cases per thousand.

Which figure is the right one?

Note on the contradictions of statistical figures
These contradictory figures must not lead us to think that stastistics are useless. One only has to know how to use them.

170

Statistics show orders of magnitude. There is an essential difference if something is true once in ten, a hundred or a thousand cases.

However those who are actually affected do not find this difference comforting. She or he is affected, no matter how frequent the problem is in the population.

The scale of frequency of cerebral palsy shows the general importance of this problem. From this point of view there is no difference if we talk about one damaged child in 250 or in 500 births. The number of newborn children with cerebral palsy is counted in every thousand births. In countries with a high birth rate (30 births per 1000 inhabitants) the problem of motor disturbance arises when inhabitants number at least 10 000. Therefore even with a low birth rate there are several hundred cases a year in countries with 10 million inhabitants. Most of these children survive. When motor-disturbed children up to ten years of age are taken into account too, we get a total number of several thousand. Because of the highly developed health services in our industrialised nations more and more severely damaged children survive. If we widen our group to children of under 15 and presume a higher birth rate, we come near to the figures which were calculated for the USA in the 1940s.

One must not underestimate the exactness of statistical figures.

Any attempt to try and help all affected people in institutes will be doomed to failure, because of their very large number, whether they are half a million or "only" 100,000.

Many specialists believe that most motor-disturbed children have no chance of ever surpassing the level of achievement of young children.

This notion is wrong as many of these children can recover entirely if their mothers start Conductive Education early enough and practise it under optimal conditions. (A child is "entirely recovered" when his level of achievement shows no essential difference to that of other children of the same age.)

Many specialists and institutions try to help those affected and their parents.

But now there is a real chance to overcome this problem and this is due to the little German girl Dina.

She was severely motor-disturbed, her hands and feet were affected; from her fifth month onwards she did exercises according to the Vojta method and for a short time according to the Bobath method. That was when her mother Caroline Seiffer wrote me (K.A.) a letter and asked me for help. She asked me whether her little daughter who was then 20 months old would ever be able to walk, sit and stand. This was the beginning of the "case of Dina".

In March 1985 Dina's mother travelled from the Baltic to Budapest to show us photos and specialists' reports about her daughter, but she did not bring Dina with her.

Dina was not then able to grip, her hands being clenched in fists. She could not roll from her stomach onto her back, nor the other way round.

When we realized that Dina could not be brought to the Petö Institute in Budapest once a month for instruction, my wife and I had to look for another solution. We did not want to leave her without help and explained to the mother why it was no use doing passive exercise. Instead we told her to play a lot with her child, and we showed her some games.

Shortly after that Frau Seiffer wrote to us and told us that Dina was totally changed: the lethargic child had become lively.

This change decisively influenced the mother who went on as she had begun. And so she also influenced us very strongly. The reports about Dina became more and more fascinating. The mother's questions continually put forward new problems which we tried to clarify in long letters.

In September we saw Dina for the first time. Frau Seiffer brought her to Budapest to show her to us.

In March 1986 they came to Budapest again for two weeks and went to the Institute for two hours a day. Before that we prepared the mother for her task and talked about her experiences afterwards.

Dina learns to walk between two poles. Her mother supports the position of her left wrist.

The result of this "correspondence course" can be seen by the fact that when she returned to Budapest in September, she was accompanied by another German mother who had a daughter, about the same age as Dina, with cerebral palsy affecting her arms and legs. Both mothers went to the Institute for three weeks, six hours a day.

As we were already involved in this problem-solving approach for two children we wrote a booklet for mothers with children with cerebral palsy, about Conductive Education (see part I of this volume).

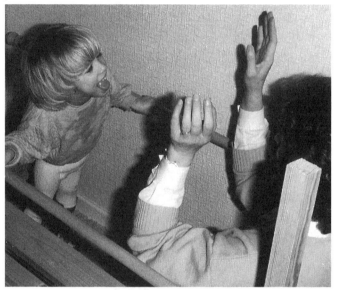

Dina needs no support on her wrists. Her mother wants her to lift her arms all by herself. (There are some things wrong with the plinth: not being made of beech, it is too hard; the slats are too broad in relation to the child's hands; the edges are not rounded. This is why Dina does not really like to grip them.)

Now Dina is three-and-a-half years old. She can sit on an ordinary chair at the table when eating, although she sometimes needs a bit of help with eating itself. She can stand on her own, when she can hold on to something. She can also walk when she is supported at the hands or at the trunk or when she can hold on to the back of a light chair and push it forwards. She is very lively and is interested in everything that goes on around her. She often asks her mother to help her to reach a certain goal. When standing and walking her legs sometimes still cross. If, however, her mother tells her to correct the position of her legs, she understands and corrects it. The other girl is developing well, too.

Everybody who knows her, especially of course her mother, enjoys Dina's cheerful nature, her liveliness, her entire positive development. We feel that she has activated, even changed us, too. She totally changed her mother's life, to whom this development is due. Day by day Frau Seiffer can see the immense importance of her cooperation with the child. It is true that she needed our support, but the success is due to her direct influence on her daughter.

We could see what fantastic results came of the problematic "correspondence course". Up until then success with the Petö System required input from specialist conductors, who had had a four-year training, both practical and theoretical. Here a mother was able to promote her child's development just with a little written support, and to adapt her education to changing needs.

This can certainly be explained in theory, but nevertheless it is astonishing that it happens in reality.

Success with the Petö System requires a continuous, uninterrupted process of learning that makes it possible to overcome the cerebral dysfunction. This process, which has to last the whole day, produces a gradual reduction in symptoms and finally makes them disappear. In the Petö Institute the conductors support this learning process. They observe the children's activities and guide them with appropriate instructions.

This consistency in education is a natural and self-evident task for the mother of a healthy infant and is fulfilled unconsciously; neither is it a problem for the mother of a handicapped child.

A further essential precondition for success with the Petö System is the child's own activity. Children will only learn if they strive actively for a goal and reach it. In this way the activity leading to the goal is learned. The conductor's task is to recognize what the child strives for, or to turn her attention to a goal which the conductor knows from past experience will be interesting for the child, and to help her reach this goal. The child must reach her goal as a result of her own efforts, although at first the conductor will have to help. The amount of help can be gradually reduced and the child's independence will increase correspondingly. In this way the child will learn to conquer the symptoms of her brain damage.

Each mother educates her child spontaneously in this way without being aware of it. This makes the child more independent and she learns to talk. Normally this process goes on without being really noticed.

This apparently spontaneous development will get stuck with a motor-disturbed child, since the mother does not get the "conduction" from her child which she needs for her educational activity. If however she gets the appropriate help for her education and if she is therefore made aware of her educational tasks, she will be able to recognize what the child really wants - in spite of her limited activity - and how she can encourage her to reach her goals. Thus the child's achievements will gradually increase through learning and her symptoms disappear. So the mother succeeds in transforming her child's general process of education successfully and quickly into "Pető education".

The success of the mother's practising of Conductive Education lies in the way the mother learns to combine the child's motivations with the creation of the conditions which are needed in order to overcome her difficulties.

But soon another problem arose: Dina reached her third year and began to be actively interested in children of the same age. Now she needed to play in a group, but her level of achievement was not high enough yet to be able to go to a regular kindergarten and play with healthy children. It was not right either to bring her into contact with mentally handicapped and autistic children, as these children are not able to play with Dina in a way which is supporting her development. This kind of play however is the most effective condition for the rehabilitation of motor-disordered children at the Pető Institute.

From the point of view of Conductive Education it would be a grave mistake to disregard Dina's new motivation towards co-operation with other children. The former great successes were achieved because the mother integrated her daughter's needs into her educational activities and satisfied them. How can she get an appropriate group for Dina together? If Steffi were living near her, this would be easy; but the two families live far apart. This problem has to be solved, too.

These are our ideas concerning this problem: There certainly are other families who have children of Dina's age with cere-bral palsy, who live near the Seiffer family. If some of these children and their mothers could meet Dina and her mother for one or two hours a day, there would be a special, conductive, provisional children's group. Frau Seiffer would learn to recog-nize the opportunities in group games for Dina's development and how to use them. Actually she does not have to do anything essentially different from what she has done before; there is only one factor added: the motivation for playing in a group. A basic condition for the right group is that the other children co-operate actively with each other. In the interest of her child's further development, Frau Seiffer should help other mothers to understand and practise Conductive Education, so they can en-courage their children's development. This will be facilitated by Dina's positive example. Each meeting would also give the mothers the opportunity for intensive exchange of experiences.

If the group, which at first will consist of two or three child-ren, effects a rapid and obvious development in the children, soon more children will come and later on there will be more such groups. Thus the "case of Dina" could trigger off a move-ment of mothers, who join together in fighting against the motor disturbances of their children. The younger children with the best starting points will experience an entire "metamor-phosis" and be accepted in a regular kindergarten or school.

The mothers whose children became entirely healthy are expected to convey their experience to two or three other mothers or to help and inform in conductive kindergartens. Thus more and more infants with cerebral palsy will be healed at or before reaching kindergarten age. Only the children who were not treated according to Petö early enough or who kept their symptoms in spite of their mother's education - no matter for what reason - will have to be admitted to the Petö Institute for rehabilitation and will attend regular school later.

Of course there are technical problems as well. A kindergarten will need rooms, equipment, toys etc. It is however surprising how simple the things necessary for the Petö System are. A simple chair will suffice to teach a child to sit down, to sit and to get up. She can hold on to at the back of the chair and so learn to stand and to walk. She can climb onto the chair, and with a bit of imagination one can invent a lot of games with the chair. If you have a ladder-back chair made or make one yourself, you should make sure that the rungs go down to the floor between the back legs. This cannot be done with an expensive wheel-chair. There are many ways of using such simple but cleverly designed equipment. Unfortunately they cannot be bought anywhere. One should not make the mistake and wait for an institutional solution, but try to find people who are ready to help among one's family and acquaintances. The "societies of metamorphosis" will consist of mothers, families, helpful friends and obliging people and support the mothers and their children.

That is exactly the core of the "case of Dina". The little girl grows and develops and thus creates new tasks all the time; tasks which affect not only the family but also a constantly increasing circle of people who are interested in the solution to the problems of children with cerebral palsy. Dina's development will require certain cooperation by these people. We, too, feel motivated by her. We never dreamt about writing a booklet for the mothers, but we had to do it. Then we realized that conductive, transitory kindergartens would be required. We suppose we will have to contribute to their existence by our presence and encouragement. There will be new problems when the group of mothers, children and supporters becomes bigger. The zest of this movement will attract more and more specialists. There will be more and more people who need help, but human distress will mobilise the wish to help. The affected children dictate the pace of the movement by their growth and development. Time is pressing! Dina is already three-and-a-half years old.

Note: There was no reaction to this urgent call for help for Dina.

26 May 1987

To Susanne Gross:

It is already summer, that means it is time for Steffi to be freed from her nappies. During the day you should not put nappies on her any more, but put her on her potty regularly at the same time: in the morning after waking up, at about ten o'clock before she gets something to eat, at one o'clock before lunch, at four before dinner and at eight before putting her to bed. It is very important to keep to these times. When you go somewhere with Steffi, always take her potty with you. Habitual actions will be integrated into the brain function. Dr Pető called it "conditioning". Praise Steffi when sitting on the potty has the expected success. In this way she will soon tell you when she has to go on the potty. It is not urgent yet for her to be trained, but it should not be put off too long by putting her in nappies, as then she will not realize when she has wet herself.

I hope Steffi has recovered. Resistance to illness can be increased by swimming. Take care however that she is not scared. The best way to get her used to water is by letting her splash around. When taking her out of the water rub her well with a towel. This stimulation to her skin will make her stronger too.

Try to make Steffi stamp her foot when standing or walking with the Petö boots. She should lift one knee and then stamp loudly with her foot. Of course this has to happen on hard ground. Invent a game where she can stamp, and an appropriate rhyme.

Try also to invent games in which she has to walk by alternately holding onto pieces of furniture. She should sit down without her boots using the ladder-back chair, by gripping one rung after the other, then get up again the same way. This is important for learning to walk independently.

These instructions are also important for Dina, so please send a copy of this letter to Caroline.

6 June 1987

From Caroline Seiffer:

... We already talked about the problems Dina has with walking. I have so far not been able to overcome my disappointment, as I had put a lot of hope into Dina's activities. Of course I noticed that her arms and upper trunk remained inactive, at least to a large extent, but I thought it could be changed more easily. The day after my visit to you, I had a talk with the group leader, the head of department and a translator in the Institute. I was told that they think that Dina could well learn to move in a room, but they were not sure whether she would ever be able to walk in the streets. I was so shocked about this that I forgot to ask whether this was a final diagnosis or if it only applied to the near future. I was also told that my goal until October should be for Dina to be able to walk along the furniture.

I read your letter again and again and now realize that I have to watch her arms more consistently. We walk through the flat and I only hold her by the hands. This works quite well. But when we go to the playground, I sometimes let her walk for a short while just holding her at the shoulders, not at the hips or the trunk any more. I then put her on a slide on her tummy and she enjoys sliding down on her own.

My efforts to get a group together have had no success yet. I am neither supported by the paediatrician, nor by the centre for handicapped people, nor by the kindergarten for physically handicapped children. They seem to be actually afraid that I could woo patients away from them.

After my return I got a letter saying I have to enrol Dina at the kindergarten for the handicapped at O. (20 miles from here) from her fourth birthday. She would be fetched by the bus at 8 a.m. and brought back at about 2 p.m. I have told them before that we would not send her to that kindergarten and when I now repeated my decision I was warned against the possible results of such "isolation".

I contacted our normal kindergarten here in town and probably I will be allowed to take Dina there for an hour once or twice a week for singing, fingergames and so on. I could lead this.

I enclose the letter from a Frau Brosch. I want to tell you about her before you start reading it. Frau Brosch heard about me from my former physiotherapist during a stay at the Baltic. Her family lives 450 miles from here. Frau Brosch had many bad experiences with hospitals and physicians, but has not given up hope yet. I sent her your booklet. She wants to practise Conductive Education in any case. She has written down everything she thought important and hopes that you will be able to answer her letter. (*This happened.*) She and her husband will come to see us at the end of June, together with their child, and I will be better able to explain everything to her. She also wrote to Dr Hári and asked for an appointment, if possible together with Susanne and me. This mother would be exactly the right person for working in a group, but she lives even further away than Susanne. But she plans to come here for a few weeks, since it is so important for her.

I telephoned Susanne... Steffi has had bad bronchitis again and is now treated with a medicine to prevent further infections, as in fact she has been ill since December 1986. She is already able to stand at her chair and play for half an hour.

To Caroline Seiffer:

...We are concerned that you seem unnecessarily worried obout Dina's development, but you can remain optimistic for future. What you were told about the practical tasks in the In- stitute was right; however attention was focussed too strongly

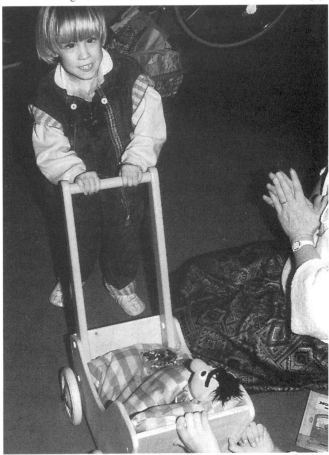

Dina pushing a doll's pram with a weight inside.

on walking. The mother should be concerned with her child's entire personality. What you were told about Dina's walking in the street is incomprehensible to us.

We never doubted that Dina will be able to walk in the street on her own. You have to make up your mind which the most important tasks are, as they change all the time. You have already succeeded in teaching Dina to reach her goal by walking. This is a great credit to your effort.

Now you must consciously improve on this achievement. It is right to help Dina from the front when at home. Please make sure Dina is gripping your fingers and not you hers. This is a huge difference and you should be aware of it.

It is your educational goal to teach Dina to walk on her own. This can only be achieved step by step. One of these steps is when Dina is holding your fingers, another one when she is for example holding a short stick horizontally with both her hands and is standing with you opposite her, stabilising her so she feels secure. Later on it will be enough if you support Dina's grip with only one hand while your other open hand just touches hers. If Dina sways, use both your hands again so she can regain her balance.

At present it is enough if Dina holds the stick with both hands (later just with one) while you hold one end and walk at her side. You can also walk in the street with her like this.

Such little steps in learning are temporary stages on the way to independent walking. There are other approaches, of course. Try different possibilities and when the goal, the intended natural movement, is reached, you have found the right way.

All this is a game for Dina, that is she sets herself goals and reaches them. This will give you ample opportunity for your education programme. One of your educational aims is independent walking. This also means that Dina should hold onto furniture and step sideways to reach her goal. In this process it is most important for Dina to learn to reach her goal through her own efforts. At the same time she will solve intermediate tasks, for example opening the legs, correcting or preventing crossing of the legs, slackening the grip to grasp another thing, and so on.

You encourage her in this, first through motivation, that is the choices of aims, and then change her education gradually in a way that matches Dina's increasing ability. When her legs do not cross and touch each other when moving forward, when she can take a few steps forward without holding on, then independent walking has begun. However, before reaching this phase Dina must be able to move her arms spontaneously so that she can protect herself in case she falls. This is another educational goal: Dina must learn to fall. (Shift her weight to the front and go down to a squatting position with her head up and hands open, stretched out in front.) The things she learns at home she will also be able to perform in the street, but there is nothing to hold onto. This is just a transient problem, which can be solved with a stick, for example.

Perhaps we worried you by wanting to explain how important it is for Dina to integrate her arms and hands into her body image in as rapid and lasting a way as possible. We only did this to show the general importance of this problem. At present this will not be an educational goal for long as Dina will quickly learn to use her hands and arms in many ways. Then the next educational goals will arise. We want to help you to recognize the arrival of new phases of education so you will get your priorities right. In this way Dina's achievement level will gradually rise.

Do not get scared! You are totally right not to take Dina to the kindergarten and leave her alone for half the day without being there. It might be good for you to try it, however, as you might have an uneasy feeling if you did not do it. It could be that Dina gets accustomed to the new surroundings. You need to talk about it instead of talking about a "danger of isolation", which is absolutely absurd as Dina lives in a home which is very advantageous from a relational-psychological point of view. She has a mother who does a lot with her, a father and two sisters. How can anyone call this isolation? It might be more harmful to spend the time from 8 am to 2 pm in the company of strangers. Dina has to get used to new surroundings gradually and anyway the educators in the kindergarten do not know a thing about Conductive Education.

Dina is still only starting to overcome her difficulties. If she develops a new form of movement, it is only you who can immediately recognize, encourage and correct it. Try to put yourself in her position and imagine the problems which will probably arise, how Dina will be able to solve them and how you can encourage her to do it. You recognize new problems, find solutions and ways of correcting her. Because of this everybody taking part in Dina's education should rely on your observations.

We like the idea of the regular kindergarten in your village much more. I think it will be good at the beginning to go there once or twice a week for just an hour and to do things with her there. It would be very good if the kindergarten teacher could form a group for Dina with two or three quiet children. If she is interested in Dina's development this might well be the grain of a conductive kindergarten, as Dina's example will attract parents of children with similar problems...

By the way what about the "case of Dina"? You intended to show your essay to the Spastics Society and send it to a journal for the parents of handicapped children. It is only moral support that can protect these children from bureaucratic opposition.

It is a pity Steffi is ill so often. But it was very good to hear that she is already able to play for half an hour when standing. Is she able to walk with the boots? Susanne should teach her...

We enclosed the copy of our answer to Frau Brosch. It would be very interesting and probably very good for both children if Frau Brosch and her child could come to you for a few weeks.

From Caroline Seiffer:

Yesterday the Brosch family was here and I want to tell you about it immediately.

As I already told you I was grateful to receive your letter.

Your encouragement is always very important for me; sometimes I think that everything gets too much, but then it is okay again. Dina and I practise walking only at the chair now and from the front. We have stopped walking the other way. I realized that there was a lot that was wrong with it. When we walk supporting her from the front, Dina only takes my fingers; in this way we can easily walk 100 metres. I have to correct her legs less often. We like to walk to the slide in the playground, this is a good motivation. At home we walk with the chair; I am worried about her leaning to one side. She leans to the left, even when standing. It is not so noticeable when she walks with my hand, but rather when walking with the chair. The left leg seems to me to be a bit shorter, but the X-rays showed that there is nothing wrong with her hips. I think this is because of strong tension on the left side. What do you think?

Gripping is getting better and I make sure that she is always busy with both hands.

She "talks" a lot now, but besides "Elsie" and sometimes "Hanne" she is still quite incomprehensible. One can see that she understands things more and more; not only does she answer with "no" or shaking her head or "ham" (means "yes") when being asked, but she also does so in a game when she is given something that does not belong to the game.

On the whole I am quite content.

On 7 July Steffi will be operated on. I think they will take out her adenoids and probably her tonsils. The doctor said that this was why she always had a cold, and also she breathed through the mouth instead of the nose. Originally Susanne and Steffi wanted to come here in July, but I am not sure if this will happen.

Dina walking on the beach with her mother. She walks several hundred metres a day when supported from the front or the back.

Now something about Frau Brosch and her child. We talked on the phone several times before she came, and she seemed to be very interested. I am not sure whether this will still be the case after the visit.

The Broschs have such a negative attitude towards progress that I cannot cope with it. They will not believe anything any more.

Little Sylvia is a type similar to Steffi, very limp with sporadic spasms. Her eyes do not fix very well, most of the time she looks upwards to the side with both eyes, but her gaze can be attracted with toys. The way her mother carries and feeds her is totally wrong. When being fed she lies on the arm, her head bent backwards; the mother pushes the food into her mouth so Sylvia only has to swallow it and yet she closes her mouth very well. She only drinks, or rather sucks, from a feeding cup. She is held with her head fixed backwards. She holds her head very badly.

I told the parents that I used to do all those things wrong as well and how you helped me to do things correctly. They both repeated: "Sylvia cannot do that. This is the only way for her to eat, otherwise she will not accept food." They said Sylvia was not able to grip. I put two coloured sticks into her hands and we played "Pat-a-cake,...". The parents only said that this was a lucky coincidence, she could not do it. Sylvia can say "mamam" and "dadad". The parents think that Sylvia does not mean them, that she does not know the meaning of these words. It was only at the end that both began to doubt.

I put Dina on the potty and suggested putting Sylvia on another potty at Dina's side. Frau Brosch said no, she said it was useless as Sylvia did not know what to do there. But I persisted and put Sylvia next to Dina. The mother stood near her, obviously waiting for her child's protest. Instead of that there was a smell after a minute and Sylvia's potty was filled.

I think both Broschs are very sceptical and cannot see Dina's advances as they did not know her before.

They are going to contact me again; perhaps they changed their minds on their long way back home.

Note on the lack of a realistic perspective

Intimidating the parents of handicapped children and destroying their hopes is not only wrong but also harmful. The parents' fears and depression are not restricted to themselves, they are not their private affairs because they may seriously

*harm their child's entire life. Not only because the mother's
mood influences the child's behaviour - even an infant of a few
weeks can react strongly to his mother's mood -, but also because hopelessness takes us away from our activity, our ability
to solve problems. A mother (or father) without hope loses the
motivation to help, she does not have the necessary strength
and remains passive.*

*Sylvia seems to be a mild case, compared to Dina in her orig-
inal state. She could certainly overcome her difficulties, if her
parents took pains to learn to develop and use their educational
ability.*

We fear that this will never happen.

I have already written to you about the professor who contacted me. She is hoping to collaborate with the Petö Institute.
She will telephone me one of these days. Perhaps this could
help me to find interested mothers. I am trying hard, but I have
the feeling that nobody believes a mother; perhaps an affected
mother would. But when I say that there is a professor who is
interested in the method, people seem to be more interested.

I contacted the physician in L. who examined Dina about a
year ago and who was very interested. This time she told me
she could do nothing for me as she did not know enough about
the method. She said your booklet was not enough and she
needed special literature. Besides she was not allowed to promote things or give away addresses.

The people in the centre for handicapped children are sceptical anyway, as I told you before.

Eva, too, sent her booklet to a physician in Munich who she
believed was interested. But he sent it back saying he could not
say anything about it, he did not know Petö and could not recommend it.

Here in Germany things will not get known and accepted if
they are not dictated from "above", if there is not a famous personality who approves of it publicly. Susanne tells me she has
the same difficulties, she has not yet found support either. I am

preparing a report for a paper which is very difficult for me. Perhaps it will be accepted...

From Susanne Gross:

...I used to put Steffi on the potty for a while with success. In spite of this she frequently wet herself. Now that I put her on it regularly, at the times you told me, it works better. Sometimes she only wets herself once a day.

Apart from this I am not very satisfied with her at the present. Her walking has got worse. There were times when she could walk quite well even without her boots but now she walks very badly. She often crosses her legs. She is very listless because of the heat. I think she feels most comfortable in a swimming pool. Steffi loves to go there but the problem is the right support for swimming. She tips forwards because she cannot keep her balance.

Next week we will go to visit Dina for five or six days...

11 July 1987

To Caroline Seiffer:

...Your report about Dina makes it clear that she is developing satisfactorily. We never give hope when it is not justified and when we criticize we hope for your understanding. This has proved to be a good way of doing it.

Dina develops, as we expected, in the right way. The difference between the two halves of her body has been there from the beginning and need not worry us, but it has always to be considered. Asymmetries like this are quite frequent with spastic children. Up until now the severe symptoms were the focus of interest. As they diminished, these minor symptoms become more conspicuous. Dina was examined by an orthopaedist several times, the X-ray showed nothing peculiar; the left hand is affected more. We think you are right in your opinion that the difference between the two sides is caused by spasticity. Your attempt to correct this by using both hands, seems to be right. Maybe you could also add this: when standing or walking at the chair, Dina should grip the rungs at the very end. The arms should be equally stretched. In this way the difference between the two sides will be eliminated. Praise Dina and tell her: "Now you're standing (walking) nicely, that's the way you should always stand (walk)." When she uses just one hand for eating, watch that she does not neglect the "clumsy" hand and ensure that she uses it as often as the other one. (Of course the left hand must not be called "clumsy"; but you already know that.) When Dina is sitting she should correct the difference between her two sides herself. This is very important for preventing scoliosis.

Asymmetry must not be regarded as permanent damage, but as an educational challenge, for which you will find a solution.

By always telling her what she is doing you have already made considerable progress. Now try to make Dina imitate the movements of your mouth. For this she has to look into your face, of course.

Your report about the Brosch family was very vivid. The girl reminds us of Steffi in her original state. She has got diplegia. I hope you managed to change the parents' unjustified pessimism. You did very well and little Sylvia cooperated with you at once astonishingly well. If the parents could be freed from their doubts and if the mother could learn to use her abilities for cooperative learning, one could count on the child's "wonderful" development with realistic optimism.

Frau Baumann wrote and told me that she could not come to the Institute until next summer, Wolfgang however needs some boots now.

I hope Steffi is healthy and will remain so, in order to be able to develop further. We expect a lot from the planned meeting of the two children.

We can understand very well that you have difficulties finding a journal which will accept your report. It is an explosive subject which is very uncomfortable for many specialists. This is why these things have to be taken slowly. If you want me to, I can look at it and propose some alterations - if necessary...

Epilogue

Here we want to bring the "case of Dina" to an end. Although we would like to report Dina's further development, every book has to have an end - only life goes on.

What can we learn from this case?

One can hardly imagine more difficult conditions for practising Conductive Education than those of Dina's case. Work could not be started until quite late, when Dina's difficulties were already very great. The mother could show Dina to us just twice a year, so once every six months we had the opportunity to talk to her personally and to give her some advice. Further help could only be conveyed in writing. However correspondence is a slow and inadequate form of communication, although we answered all letters by return post. But there was always a long time lag between a problem arising and our advice arriving. In addition there was nothing published already that might have been used, as the only authoritative book was not yet translated from Hungarian into German.

Nevertheless Dina's mother has achieved good results in overcoming her daughter's difficulties. In improved conditions she would certainly have got even better results in a relatively shorter period of time.

Solving problems would certainly have been much easier if we could have personally seen Dina's educational circumstances, at least occasionally, and have had photographs of her showing her current difficulties. Also her mother could have used extra help, at least for housework, to be able to organize Dina's day optimally. The Petö System represents a way of living in which time has to be used properly. However Dina's mother was forced to face all difficulties alone. It would have been an immense relief to her if other mothers practising the Petö System lived in the same region and they could talk about their problems. It would have also made a difference if there were specialists near who knew at least the basic principles of Conductive Education. We regret that this has not been the case so far. The mother tried to talk about her problems with other people and got - certainly with the very best of intentions - confusing advice, which more than once had a lasting influence on her. Of course it is easy to use conventional terms; more difficult, however, to think in a totally new way. The basis for successful practice of Conductive Education is a radically new way of thinking. Furthermore the mother should use Dr Petö's carefully designed equipment which is simple and has varied uses, even if it is much easier for her to get complicated, technically highly developed, expensive, but often inadequate apparatus. The child's development, however, is only helped by the former.

We hope that the mothers and fathers of motor-disordered children can learn a lot from Dina's case.

We think that the problems which have arisen, the search for solutions under very varied material conditions, the success in spite of many frustrations, in short the living reality of the "case of Dina" gives this correspondence an importance that surpasses the case at issue.

In the first three years of a child's life the mother has an exceptional influence on the development of the child's personality. She can bring about a dramatic change in the life of her motor-disordered child, if she educates him using the Petö System with patience and perseverance.

Today parents are deprived of their biological responsibilty for their children. The parents of a dysfunctional child in particular are not credited with the competence for dealing with him appropriately. It is good that parents are offered help from various institutions even before the birth. It is bad, however, that because of this the parents' right to decide is limited. We think that parents need support that enables them to see their child's situation realistically. It is especially important in the case of a motor-disordered child that the parents are able to develop an idea of their own abilities, which surpass those of all the specialists by far.

Parents should not be hindered from understanding their child's situation correctly, neither through illusions nor through force.

The Authors

The authors, Dr Károly Akos (born 1918) and his wife Magda Akos (born 1921), have been working for decades on the exploration of general functions of the brain, the temporal functioning of the human brain as a whole (human chronobiology). They were able to explain how individual consciousness develops. They studied the temporality of physiological functions of the brain as a whole and developed the psychochronographic method of examination (PCG) which allows a quantitative description of the functions of the human brain and of its physical laws and their starting points. PCG is a test of the brain function under micro-stress and at the same time the clinical function test of central fatigue or recovery.

The authors also explored the human-biological transformation of the general physiological function of the human brain, that is, the rise and development of personality. They described the intercerebral, relation-psychological group conditions of normal and abnormal development and showed the practical and theoretical meaning of this anthropogenic cooperation.

Dr Akos was a friend of Dr András Petö, with whom he co-operated scientifically. After Petö died, Dr Akos continued his work as a scientific advisor to the Petö Institute and wrote together with Dr Hári, Petö's successor as head of the Institute, the textbook Conductive Education.

Dr Akos and his wife work independently from the Petö Institute.

Dr Akos is leader of the "Research Group of Psychochronography", his wife is a senior research scientist in this group.

András Petö, this genius who was not recognized in his lifetime but who became famous in many parts of the world after his death, developed Conductive Education all by himself. As he never worked out a conductive educational theory, this was done by the authors.

Appendix
Michael - A Documentation

I want to describe the case of Michael. He is a further example of Conductive Education's marvellous possibilities if parents are encouraged to discover and use their abilities. Michael's mother has succeeded in achieving progress with her son which was thought impossible by the specialists and which astonished many of them. Yet Frau G.'s conditions were - like those of Dina's mother - the worst possible. There is neither a Petö Institute nor are there conductors in the German Federal Republic. A stay at Budapest's Petö Institute is as good as impossible as there are now thousands of parents from all over the world waiting for an appointment for assessment. Nevertheless, just two visits with Dr Károly Akos and his wife Magda Akos and extensive correspondence have meant that Frau G. has been able to set in motion her son's personality development and a considerable process of change and development in herself.

At the beginning of this book it was mentioned that the mother can be replaced by anyone with whom the child relates closely. However, generally it is the reality of our society that mothers are responsible for the upbringing of children. Therefore I want to stress once more that practising the Petö System is not meant to load the mother with yet another cost-saving burden, using up her time and her responsibility for its success. Neither do we intend to propagate a "new motherliness" or to revive the old myth of motherhood. We have to differentiate between woman's role, forced upon her by society (housekeeping, bringing up children, and so on) and the scientifically undisputed fact that the early mother-child relationship has a decisive influence on the child's development. This form of Conductive Education is possible only if the mother is supported extensively in all other areas of family life, for example by domestic help, temporary care of the other children in the family and so on. This help must be organized and may indeed be offered by local services. Through such services opportunities should be created to enable mothers in similar situations to exchange experiences. In short, what is needed is a health service orientated towards the needs of affected parents and open to their suggestions. Specialists and parents have to co-operate effectively.

Michael

Michael G. is born in February 1986, and has to be artificially respirated for ten days after birth.

What is wrong with him? "We can't tell you what's wrong with him" is the statement of the responsible physician at the University hospital.

Michael stays in hospital for four weeks. During this stay he is treated according to Vojta's method. On coming home he is not able to turn or lift his head. The diagnosis on the hospital discharge certificate is: "Probable contusion of the cervical spinal cord".

During Michael's first year of life his mother attends the University hospital twice a week for Vojta therapy; three times a day she does the prescribed exercises at home. She is also shown "handling". How best do I dress my child? How do I put him on my lap? Therapeutic exercises at home bring many difficulties with them. An infant sleeps a lot and when he is awake he is fed, cared for or simply cuddled. How can the mother introduce a programme three times a day without neglecting emotional relations with her child? This is added to the fact that Michael cries from the beginning because he does not feel well. His mother treats him in a way that is directed against his own well-being and is probably painful - certainly it is frightening - and that provokes very violent resistance.

Of course this is a heavy physical strain for the mother who sees that her child objects vehemently to this treatment and who feels instinctively that this cannot be the right way to do things.

A normal day, a normal, relaxed mother-child relationship is impossible as the therapy is always at the centre of things and determines what happens. This is really difficult and gives no enjoyment; on the contrary, necessary work is done only reluctantly as there seems to be no alternative and the mother does not want to have to reproach herself later for not having done everything in her power for her son.

The father refuses to do the Vojta exercises with his son as he cannot stand the crying and thinks that it is useless anyway as the child struggles so much against it. The grandmother too has to leave the room when the exercises are started.

The family entertains a lot and there is no time for three sets of exercises when a get-together starts in the afternoon. This gives the mother a persistent bad conscience. She cannot get her neglect of her obligations off her mind and so is unable to enjoy social events. Ultimately aversion against this therapy increases so much that Frau G. looks forward to her son's vaccinations, since the days that follow are "Vojta-free".

At five months severe scoliosis is diagnosed and marked asymmetry; the right half of the body is affected more severely. Michael gets an orthopaedic support, to which he is fastened day and night during the first year of his life. Most of the time he lies because he cannot sit.

On his first birthday he can hold his head up for a short time but not when lying on his back and being pulled up by his arms. His hands form a constant fist, he can neither grip nor open his hands voluntarily. He does not move his legs on his own.

A CT scan is carried out, which shows no brain abnormalities. The physician diagnoses a "lesion of the cervical spine at the level of C2", which she explains as a partial transverse lesion with paraplegia. The diagnosis of a second specialist consulted is: "A cerebral motor disorder".

By eighteen months Michael has a hunchback caused by the scoliosis.

The Vojta exercises continue and at the same time Bobath treatment is begun. In practice this means Vojta therapy once a week at the therapist's with these exercises done three or four times a day at home, and Bobath therapy once a week at another therapist's who also shows the mother how to dress Michael correctly.

The mother consults a well-known orthopaedic surgeon who has been recommended to her. He tells her to accept the fact that she has a very severely damaged child who will never be able to sit or walk. "The best we can aim for is that one day he may be able to drive an electric wheel-chair on his own, most probably not a mechanical one. But things may look quite different in two years."

Why does a doctor say such a thing to a mother? Does he realize what he does to her, how much he destroys?

For Frau G. all hope is now nipped in the bud. What is all the effort and strain of the different therapies for if they will not change anything at all? Her motivation has reached rock-bottom. Frau G. continues to go to the therapy as she does not know any alternative, although she thinks it is of no use as Michael resists more strongly than ever.

When she hears the orthopaedic surgeon's statement the Vojta therapist says that the demands on Michael must be lowered as he is obviously unable to perform what was previously expected of him.

It is not until Michael is twenty-one months old that the Vojta therapy is stopped, although Michael has shown no positive reactions since his first birthday and cries all the time. He is said to be a "blocker". The Bobath therapy continues.

At this point Michael has no control over his trunk, he hardly moves his legs and his right hand is not used at all.

Michael is a quiet, contented child who has no will of his own and who is satisfied with anything he gets. He is very sensitive to noise. He also weeps at the beginning of the Bobath exercises, perhaps because they take place in the same room as the Vojta therapy. After a while, however, he likes them. The therapist practices sitting and standing with him, but always in a passive way by putting him in a sitting or standing position and holding him while he plays. "He likes that because he doesn't have to do anything other than play" says Frau G. At the age of about two years Michael's control of his trunk has improved and the scoliosis is no longer so marked. The right arm is not used and just hangs down. But Michael can lift it a little if motivated, for example when he wants to show a bracelet. Otherwise he pulls this arm away when touched. He hardly moves his legs but draws them up when tickled. He sits when he can lean his back against something but soon falls to one side because he is unable to support himself. When lying on his tummy he can lift his head for a short time, but this is a great effort for him.

Michael gets a special seat, into which he is fastened when he wants to play. He likes this very much as the seat is comfortable. This is comfortable for the mother too - Michael is occupied for a while and she can do other things in the meantime. Michael also gets a board which enables him to stand. He refuses to be fastened to it, however, so it is never used.

In January 1988 Frau G. hears about Conductive Education for the first time at one of my talks and contacts me. She learns more about this fascinating approach and reads the "Booklet for Mothers" (Part I of this book). In this way she learns how a child with cerebral palsy can be taught to be clean by putting him on the potty in front of a ladder-back chair, so that he can grip one of the rungs and hold on. This is precisely her current problem: how can Michael be potty-trained? He wants to use the toilet or sit on the potty but he wants to be alone. However, this is impossible as he would fall without support.

Frau G. receives the most fantastic suggestions: all sorts of seats and constructions all of which have drawbacks. None of them are easy to handle. Some even require alterations to the toilet. This is where the idea of the ladder-back chair and the potty comes in handy! In a short time the grandfather makes just such a chair.

First try: Michael is put on the potty and the chair is positioned in front of him, so that he can hold on to a rung. The mother still helps with this but he wants to sit on the potty all by himself. When the mother lets go, however, he falls to one side. But he soon learns how to keep himself upright and is enthusiastic about being able to sit alone.

This example, together with the booklet and our talks, makes the mother realize how vital motivation and independence are in Conductive Education.

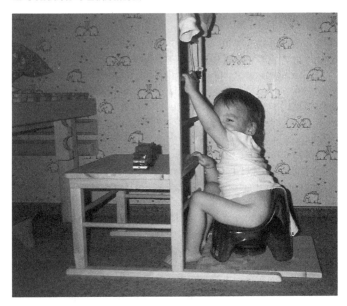

At the age of two years and four months, Frau and Herr G. take their son to Budapest. Dr Akos and his wife examine Michael, the situation is thoroughly discussed. They explain the essential elements of Conductive Education for Michael and give the parents advice and instructions (free of charge). For example, for a while Michael should sit as little as possible. Instead of having him sit the parents should play with him frequently as he lies on his back or stomach -on the floor until a plinth is made. Dr Akos would like to see the family again in two months. "It is not so much Michael who interests me, but you", he says.

The beginning is hard, as Michael likes to sit in his special chair. The mother (and the father, too, when he has the time) tries to make up games which Michael likes and which motivate him to prop himself up on his elbows and to lift his head and chest. One possible motivation, for example, is his special liking for the TV serial *Heidi*. Accordingly, his mother puts him on the floor, so that he has to prop himself up. And - unbelievable as it seems - he really succeeds in lifting his head and supporting himself for some time. It is not long before he can prop himself up safely for longer and longer, without falling to one side.

He enjoys turning himself over more and more, from back to front and over again on to his back. The better he can lie on the floor and move there the more he enjoys lying there.

His attitude towards his surroundings and everything going on around him changes too: he becomes interested in all sorts of things and soon begins to play independently, without repeating all the time that he cannot do things and that his mummy must help him. "I want to do it alone" is soon heard frequently. This of course is a great relief for the mother who now has more time for other things.

Michael undergoes a fascinating change, into a bright, interested, curious child, who discovers his own will. He is no longer content with everything put before him but vociferously expresses his displeasure and tries to get his own way.

Michael's process of personality development was set in motion by the way in which his mother did things with him. Central to this is his motivation. The mother gives him her time and attention, she is directed by his needs and success and helps him to reach his goals. The mother now feels she is on the right track as Michael has made remarkable advances in quite a short time. Encouraged by his personality development and his motor advance, she rediscovers hope and is motivated to follow the way that she has chosen more systematically and decisively.

Frau G. has always sung a lot with Michael. As she now knows how important rhythm, music, and songs are for children with cerebral palsy, she sings a lot with her son and he really enjoys this. Language plays a central role in Conductive Education. Awareness of activity and movement is brought about through language. Frau G. gradually recognizes these connections and begins to put into language everything that Michael does or that she does with him.

When Michael is two years and five months old, his parents take him to Dr Akos and his wife in Budapest for a second time. The new situation is discussed, problems and questions are settled, new instructions and advice given (again free of charge). Dr Akos and his wife are astonished at Michael's unexpectedly rapid development. They are pleased to see that now he moves his legs at will. When Frau G. tells them that he can take a little step with both legs - when he is supported, of course - Dr Akos says, "Now Michael knows that he has legs".

Michael now tries to lift his left arm when lying on his stomach supporting himself, to grasp something and get it. Soon he extends his left arm and keeps his hand open, an experience which he likes very much.

Again and again countless examples show the parents how important motivation is for Michael to be active, to be able to discover his curiosity and so to develop.

Once for example he is sitting on his potty and holding on to the ladder-back chair. Suddenly he calls his mummy who is surprised by what she sees. He has discovered that he can push the ladder-back chair away by extending his arms and bending forward, and then pull it back again. He does this dozens of times because he likes it so much.

Soon the special seat is put aside as Michael does not want to sit in it any more.

If he does not sit straight and his mother draws his attention to this by saying: "Michael, watch your sitting!" he immediately corrects his posture and sits up straight. Sometimes his left foot trembles ("clonus"); then it is enough for the mother to say "Michael, look, your foot!" to make him aware of the trembling and to stop it by pressing the foot against something.

These examples demonstrate the unity of language and consciousness. A posture, movement or activity can be made conscious through language. This creates the condition for changing them.

Michael likes to sit on a low, narrow wall in the garden if his grandfather and the children from the neighbourhood are sitting, playing or talking there. His mother used to hold him. One day he demands: "Mummy, let me go!"; the mother replies that she cannot let him go as he would certainly fall. But he insists that she lets him go and she does so, sure that she will immediately have to catch him. But Michael really sits and stays sitting: straight, supported by his legs, leaning on the fence, without supporting himself with his hands and without anyone holding him at the sides, which until then was impossible.

Michael himself can hardly believe it, he is excited, laughs and is very happy. He wants everybody to see him and seems to be sitting there for ages - at least his mother thinks so. Since then he often wants to sit on the little wall. Frau G. goes on telling him to support himself with his hands so that he can sit safely and also shows him how to do it. Sometimes he has already done it.

Michael is a poor eater; until now he has had to be fed. Recently he said he wanted to eat alone. His mother shows him how to hold a fork or spoon and to take it to his mouth. At first she supports his grip with her own hand and makes the movement with him but he soon learns to do this on his own. Since he can eat on his own he also eats more than before.

His severely affected right hand has already become easier to move and more supple. He starts opening and closing it at will if his mother supports his wrist. While doing so she talks to him.

Observation is a most essential point in the mutual teaching-and-learning process of mother and child. Frau G. always closely observes Michael's development and adapts her way of doing things and playing with him in response to this. For example, she has invented a game which forces Michael to use both his hands. His one-sidedness has diminished through these symmetric movements. The fact that Michael has had a two-handled mug for some time, which he can grasp with both hands, also helps this development. When he drinks his mother still supports his right wrist.

Each activity and each game has two goals. Firstly the child should have fun, otherwise he will neither become active nor learn anything. The other goal is to increase his ability to use his hands, arms and legs appropriately. These are basic conditions for independent standing, sitting and walking. This makes the symptoms of motor-disorder gradually disappear. It is the mother's task to bring her educational goals and her child's motivation into accord.

Again and again Frau G. takes pictures of Michael to send them to Dr Akos and his wife, together with questions and explanations of her work. We have also taken video clips and sent them to Budapest. Both Dr Akos and his wife discussed the material and gave explanations, instructions and tips in writing.

Meanwhile Frau G.'s attitude towards her son has changed decisively. Before it was his disorder which determined their relationship. He was her sick child. This was joined by self-pity (Why me?), reinforced by the pity of relatives and friends. Their whole life was overshadowed by a negative view of things, and their family life was especially affected.

Today, Michael is no longer a disordered child but is her son who needs more educational care than other children at that age. The whole situation has become more relaxed, she and Michael enjoy doing things together. There is no artificial, forced therapeutic situation any more. Not only does Michael take part voluntarily, he even develops his own ideas which inspire his mother.

The doctors, therapists, educationalists responsible for him and other parents are equally surprised at Michael's enormous progress which they had never thought possible. This has increased Frau G.'s self-confidence. She relies more and more on her own abilities and is proud of her success.

Gabriele Haug

Post script:
The mother reports happily that Michael has just taken the first steps in his life - holding on to the ladder-back chair.

The Hungarian physician and educationalist Dr András Petö (1893-1967) developed "Conductive Education" after the Second World War and founded an Institute in Budapest in 1952, now called the "Mozgássérültek Petö András Intézete" ("Petö Institute for motor-disordered people"), where conductors are now trained.

The following types of problems can be successfully helped by Conductive Education:

Children with:
-Cerebral palsy:
 Spasticity
 Athetosis
 Ataxia
 any combination of these
-Spino-motor dysfunction (lesion of the spinal cord):
 Spina bifida
-Periphero-motor dysfunction

Adults with:
-Cerebral dysfunction:
 Parkinson's disease
 Multiple sclerosis
 Hemiplegia
-Spino-motor dysfunction:
 Transverse lesion of the cord, with paraplegia

THE FOUNDATION FOR CONDUCTIVE EDUCATION

The Foundation for Conductive Education offers a growing range of materials, in written and video form, to bring you up-to-date with developments in this field. For example:

CONDUCTIVE EDUCATION by Mária Hári and Karoly Ákos (Routledge, 1988) first published in Hungarian in 1971, this translation is so far the only extensive exposition of Conductive Education from the Petö Institute where it was developed.

●

GOING TO BUDAPEST, a functional plastic satchel, containing three booklets and a variety of other materials to help families contemplating going to the Petö Institute in Budapest.

●

A GIFT FROM HUNGARY, featuring actor Bob Hoskins. A twelve-minute video on the Foundation's work to bring Conductive Education to the UK.

●

STEP BY STEP, a thirty-minute video showing the integrated day at the Foundation's Birmingham Institute, the only school outside Hungary which is run on wholly Conductive lines by fully trained conductors from the Petö Institute.

●

We stock the only comprehensive range of publications on Conductive Education in English (send for full list). We answer enquiries on specific points from parents, professionals and students, give talks to interested groups and welcome visitors who wish to find out more. You can also become a member of the Foundation or subscribe to our quarterly magazine *The Conductor*.

For further information please contact:
The National Information Centre
The Foundation for Conductive Education
P.O. Box 363
Birmingham B15 2TT

Telephone: 021-414 4947
Fax: 021-414 6278
●